How to Pass

NATIONAL 5
Biology

Billy Dickson and Graham Moffat

HODDER
GIBSON
AN HACHETTE UK COMPANY

The Publishers would like to thank the following for permission to reproduce copyright material:

Every effort has been made to trace all copyright holders, but if any have been inadvertently overlooked the Publishers will be pleased to make the necessary arrangements at the first opportunity.

Although every effort has been made to ensure that website addresses are correct at time of going to press, Hodder Gibson cannot be held responsible for the content of any website mentioned in this book. It is sometimes possible to find a relocated web page by typing in the address of the home page for a website in the URL window of your browser.

Hachette Livre UK's policy is to use papers that are natural, renewable and recyclable products and made from wood grown in sustainable forests. The logging and manufacturing processes are expected to conform to the environmental regulations of the country of origin.

Orders: please contact Bookpoint Ltd, 130 Park Drive, Abingdon, Oxon OX14 4SE. Telephone: (44) 01235 827720. Fax: (44) 01235 400454. Lines are open 9.00–5.00, Monday to Saturday, with a 24-hour message answering service. Visit our website at www.hoddereducation.co.uk. Hodder Gibson can be contacted direct on: Tel: 0141 848 1609; Fax: 0141 889 6315; email: hoddergibson@hodder.co.uk

First published in 2013 by
Hodder Gibson, an imprint of Hodder Education,
An Hachette UK Company,
2a Christie Street
Paisley PA1 1NB

Impression number   5 4 3 2 1

Year   2017 2016 2015 2014 2013

Cover photo © Eric Isselée – Fotolia.com
Illustrations by Aptara, Inc.
Typeset in 13/15 Cronos Pro (Light) by Aptara, Inc.
Printed in Spain
A catalogue record for this title is available from the British Library
ISBN: 978 1 4441 8454 9

Contents

Introduction   v

Unit 1 Cell Biology

Key Area 1.1   Cell structure   1

Key Area 1.2   Transport across cell membranes   5

Key Area 1.3   Producing new cells   12

Key Area 1.4   DNA and the production of proteins   16

Key Area 1.5   Proteins and enzymes   19

Key Area 1.6   Genetic engineering   23

Key Area 1.7   Photosynthesis   27

Key Area 1.8   Respiration   32

Practice Course Assessment   **39**

Unit 2 Multicellular Organisms

Key Area 2.1   Cells, tissues and organs   47

Key Area 2.2   Stem cells and meristems   51

Key Area 2.3a   Control and communication: nervous system   54

Key Area 2.3b   Control and communication: endocrine system   60

Key Area 2.4   Reproduction   63

Key Area 2.5   Variation and inheritance   66

Key Area 2.6a   The need for transport in plants   71

Key Area 2.6b   The need for transport in animals: circulation   74

Key Area 2.6c   The need for transport in animals: gas exchange and nutrient absorption   80

Key Area 2.7   Effects of lifestyle choices on human transport and exchange systems   85

Practice Course Assessment   **92**

Unit 3 Life on Earth

Key Area 3.1   Biodiversity and the distribution of life   97

Key Area 3.2   Energy in ecosystems   102

Key Area 3.3   Sampling techniques and measurement of abiotic and biotic factors   109

Key Area 3.4   Adaptation, natural selection and the evolution of species   114

Key Area 3.5   Human impact on the environment   119

Practice Course Assessment   **128**

Skills of Scientific Inquiry   133

Your Assignment   150

Your Exam   153

Glossary   157

General introduction

Welcome to *How To Pass National 5 Biology*!

The fact that you have opened this book and are reading it shows that you want to pass your SQA National 5 Biology course. This is excellent because passing, and passing well, needs that type of attitude. It also shows you are getting down to the revision that is *essential* to pass and get the best grade possible.

The idea behind this book is to help you to pass, and if you are already on track to pass, it can help you improve your grade. It can help boost a C into a B or a B into an A. It cannot do the work for you, but it can guide you in how best to use your limited time.

In producing this book we have assumed that you have followed an SQA National 5 Level Biology course at school or college this year and that you have probably, but not necessarily, worked on Science Experiences and Outcomes up to and including Fourth Level at an earlier stage.

We recommend that you download and print a copy of National 5 level Biology Course Assessment Specification from the SQA website at www.sqa.org.uk.

You should note that in your exam only the material included in the contents tables on pages 8–12 of the Course Assessment Specification can be examined. Skills of scientific inquiry described on page 8 are also examined. You should get copies of any specimen or past papers that are available on the SQA website.

We have tried to keep the language simple and easy to understand and have used the language of SQA National 5 support materials. This is the language used in the setting of the exam papers.

Although we have covered the entire National 5 course within these materials, we have tried to emphasise those areas that cause most difficulty for students. We have concentrated on support for the examination element of the course assessment, which is worth 80% of your final grade. The other 20% is covered in your assignment and you will have support for this from school or college, although we have provided some material in the short chapter on pages 150–152.

We suggest that you use this book throughout your course. Use it at the end of each Key Area covered in class, at the end of each Unit in preparation for your Unit assessment, before your preliminary examination and, finally, to revise the whole course in the lead up to your final examination.

There is a grid on page x that you can use to record and evaluate your progress as you finish each Unit.

Course assessment outline

The National 5 Biology course is assessed in three parts: the National Units, an assignment and a course examination. It is necessary to pass *all* assessments to achieve a course award. The grading of the course award (A, B, C or D) comes from the assignment and course exam marks.

National Units

Each of the three National Units is assessed at your school or college on a pass or fail basis. There are different methods of Unit assessment. Each school or college will have its own approach but all students have to pass a short test in each Unit, write up an experiment they have carried out and also produce a short research report of about 50–100 words. Your school or college will assess the Units and you will probably have a chance to try Unit assessments again if you need to. You must pass all three Units.

Assignment (20 marks)

The assignment is a task which is based on some research that you have carried out in class time. The investigation will be supervised by your teacher and you will have to write up the work in the form of a report during a controlled assessment. During the controlled assessment you will have access to your research material and notes but you cannot use a draft copy of your assignment report.

The assignment has two stages:

1 A research stage which involves the following points:
   • selecting a relevant topic related to a key area of National 5 Biology
   • deciding on a specific aim
   • identifying sources of information and data
   • gathering information and data.
2 A communication stage which involves the following points:
   • selecting and processing relevant, reliable and unbiased information and data from your sources
   • producing a report of 500–800 words under controlled assessment conditions.

The assignment report

The report is marked out of 20 marks, allocated as shown in the table below. There are 14 marks for skills and 6 marks for the application of biological knowledge.

Aspect of your report	Marks
Stating your aim	1
Showing how your topic impacts on the environment or society	2
Selecting your sources of information and data	2
Selecting relevant information and data from your sources	2
Processing and presenting your information and data	6
Drawing a valid conclusion	1
Applying your knowledge and understanding of biology	3
Structuring your report	3
Total	**20**

The assignment is marked by SQA and makes up 20% of your overall course assessment and grading. We have provided a grid on page x that will allow you to check that you are prepared for the controlled assessment and have carried it through.

Course examination (80 marks)

The National 5 examination is a single paper consisting of a booklet of questions in two sections:

- **Section A** contains 20 multiple-choice questions for 1 mark each.
- **Section B** contains a mixture of restricted- and extended-response questions for a total of 60 marks. Restricted-response questions have a single mark while extended-response questions have 2 or 3 marks, and some might have choice within them.

The majority of the marks (50–60) test knowledge, with an emphasis on the application of knowledge. The remainder (20–30) test the application of scientific inquiry skills.

The Course examination is marked by SQA and contributes 80% to the overall grade for the course.

The various components of the National 5 Biology assessment system are as follows:

National 5 Biology	Assessment	Who does the assessing?
Units (pass or fail)	Unit 1 Tests	School staff
	Unit 2 Tests	School staff
	Unit 3 Tests	School staff
Course (graded A–D)	Assignment (worth 20% of the grade)	Marked by SQA out of 20 marks
	Examination (worth 80% of the grade) 20 multiple-choice and 60 restricted- and extended-response questions	Marked by SQA out of 80 marks

About this book

The course content section is split into three chapters, which cover the three Units of National 5 Biology. Each chapter is divided into Key Areas. Each Key Area has four features.

Key points !

These list and expand the content statements from the SQA specification using words and phrases needed to answer examination questions. Where a key term appears for the first time it is in **bold** and you will find it listed in the Glossary on pages 157–166. It is essential to read the glossary definitions when working with the key points. After having worked on a Key Area, the key points should be easy to understand. You might want to use the boxes to show progress. We suggest marking like this – if you are having difficulty, like this + if you have done further work and are more comfortable and this ✱ if you are confident you have learned a particular idea. Alternatively you could traffic light them using coloured dots – red for 'not understood', orange for 'more work needed' and green for 'fully understood'. ☐

Summary notes

These give a summary of the knowledge required in each Key Area. You must read these carefully. You could use a highlighter pen to emphasise certain words or phrases and you might want to add your own notes in the margin in pencil. In these summary notes we have tried to give examples of the biology from life situations. There are diagrams to illustrate many of the key learning ideas. Some areas contain separate boxes to show selected links to other Key Areas in the Course or sometimes to emphasise ethical issues raised by modern biology.

Hints & tips ★

Where we offer a tip to help learning it is boxed like this. These tips can be very general or can be specific to the content of the Key Area. Many are suggestions — don't feel you need to use them all.

Questions ?

These are designed to help you assess your knowledge and understanding of the key points and should be attempted on separate paper. Mark your own work using the answers provided towards the end of each Unit. Good performance in these tests is a sign of learning and progress in the Course. The questions are in two parts:

- Part A is a set of restricted-response questions. These straightforward questions start with 'name', 'state' or 'give' and can usually be answered quickly with a word or two. They would be worth 1 mark each in a Course exam.
- Part B is a set of extended-response questions. The questions start with 'describe' or 'explain' and require several lines to answer fully. In your exam there may be a choice given in extended-response questions. We suggest that, in practice, it is better to cover all options, so we have *not* included choice. These questions would be worth 2 or 3 marks in a Course exam.

Practice assessment

We have included a practice assessment linked to each Unit. These can give you an idea of your overall progress in the Course. We have designed these assessments to be like mini Course exams with multiple-choice, and restricted- and extended-response questions.

The questions are intended to replicate the types to expect in the Course exam. They allow you to judge how you are doing overall. There is a combination of questions testing knowledge and its application and some testing skills of scientific inquiry, which have been indicated with 'SSI' so that you can identify them. These are provided in roughly the same proportion as in your final exam.

Give yourself a maximum of 60 minutes to complete each test.

Mark your own work using the answers provided at the end of each Unit. Although Units are not graded, you could grade your work as you go along to give you an idea of how well you are doing in the Course. The table below shows a suggested grading system:

Mark out of 40	Grade
15–19 marks	D
20–27 marks	C
28–34 marks	B
35+ marks	A

Skills of scientific inquiry: three approaches

This section offers three different approaches to revising and improving your skills of scientific inquiry. In the first, we offer some classified tips and hints for tackling exam questions. The second approach involves six practice questions, two from each Unit, in which all the individual skills have been identified for you so that you can work to your strengths and improve weaker areas. The third approach focuses on one investigation and provides questions about the thinking that should go into experimental design. Most students should use all three sections. Answers are provided at the end of the section.

Your assignment

We give an introduction to the assignment, some suggestions for suitable topics and some information, with hints, to help you complete the task. On page x is a grid on which to record evidence for your controlled assessment.

Your exam

We give some hints on approaches to your final exams in general as well as more specific tips for your National 5 Biology exam.

Glossary

Here we have given the meanings of the special terms that occur in the Assessment specification for National 5 Biology in the context of the Key Areas where they first appear in the book. You could use this glossary to make flash cards. A flash card has the term on one side and the definition on the other. Get together with a friend and use these cards to test each other.

Answers

Short answers are provided for all of the questions in this book. These are intended to replicate SQA standard answers but we have tried to keep the answers short, and any instructions simple, to make them easier to use – there will be other acceptable answers. The answers can be found after the last Key Area in each unit.

Record of progress and self-evaluation

Use the grid below to record and evaluate your progress as you finish each of the three Units.

Feature	As an indicator of progress, I have...	Unit 1	Unit 2	Unit 3
Key points	used the minus (−), plus (+) and star (✱) system to identify areas of strength and areas requiring further attention for each of the Key Points sections			
Summary notes	read and thought about the summary notes for each Key Area and used highlighters to pick out the main points			
Hints & tips	read and thought about the hints and tips and exam technique advice for each Unit			
Questions	answered, marked and corrected the restricted-response questions at the end of each Key Area of each Unit			
	answered, marked and corrected the extended-response questions at the end of each Key Area of each Unit			
Practice assessment	answered and marked Section A of the Practice Assessment (10 multiple-choice marks for each Unit)			
	answered and marked Section B of the Practice Assessment (30 restricted- and extended-response marks for each Unit)			
Skills of scientific inquiry	read and thought about the tips given for each of the skills for each Unit			
	answered, marked and corrected the skills questions in each Unit			
Glossary	used the glossary terms and definitions to create a set of flash cards for each Unit			

Assignment evidence checklist

Your preparation for the communication stage of your assignment should allow you to produce a report which has evidence of the following assessment points.

Assessment point	Evidence	Check
Topic	My topic is related to a Key Area of N5 Biology	
	I have shown that my topic has impact on the environment or society	
Aim	I have devised and stated my aim	
	I have described clearly what is being investigated	
Selecting	I have selected relevant sources	
	My information and data come from at least **two** sources	
	My sources are reliable and credible	
Processing	I have processed my information and raw data by summarising, performing calculations and have ordered my material appropriately	
Presenting	My information is presented in at least **two** different formats	
	At least **one** of my formats is a graph, table, chart or diagram	
	My graphs, tables, charts or diagrams are labelled	
	I have compared information or data from at least **two** sources	
Concluding	I have drawn a valid conclusion which is supported by evidence from my research	
Applying biological knowledge	My report shows my knowledge and understanding of the biology involved in my topic	
Structuring report	My report has an informative title and sub-headings	
	My report is 500–800 words in length and is clear and concise	
	I have provided at least **two** references to my sources	

Cell Biology

Key Area 1.1
Cell structure

Key points !

1   A **unicellular** organism has one single cell. ☐

2   A **multicellular** organism is made up of many cells. ☐

3   The **ultrastructure** of a cell is its fine structure as revealed at high magnification. ☐

4   The ultrastructure of an animal cell includes its **cell membrane, nucleus, cytoplasm, mitochondria** and **ribosomes**. ☐

5   The ultrastructure of a plant cell includes its **cell wall**, cell membrane, nucleus, cytoplasm, sap **vacuole**, mitochondria and ribosomes. ☐

6   **Chloroplasts** are present in green plant cells. ☐

7   The ultrastructure of a **fungal cell** includes its cell wall, cell membrane, nucleus, cytoplasm, vacuole, mitochondria and ribosomes. ☐

8   The ultrastructure of a **bacterial cell** includes its cell wall, cell membrane, cytoplasm, **plasmids** and ribosomes. ☐

9   The nucleus contains genetic material (**DNA**) and controls cell activities. ☐

10 The cell membrane controls the entry and exit of substances into and out of the cell. ☐

11 Cell **organelles**, such as nuclei, mitochondria and chloroplasts, are compartments found in the cytoplasm and are the site of chemical reactions. ☐

12 Bacterial cells do not contain organelles. ☐

13 The cell wall is for support and shape and prevents plant cells from bursting. ☐

14 Plant, fungal and bacterial cell walls have different structures and are composed of different chemicals. ☐

15 The vacuole stores a watery solution of salts and sugars and helps to support cells. ☐

16 Chloroplasts contain **chlorophyll** and are the sites of **photosynthesis**. ☐

17 Mitochondria are the sites of **aerobic respiration** in cells. ☐

18 Ribosomes are the sites of **protein** synthesis in cells. ☐

19 In bacterial cells, plasmids hold some of the genetic material (DNA) of the cell. ☐

Summary notes

Living organisms and cells

The bodies of living organisms are made up of cells. Living organisms are either unicellular, with only one cell, or multicellular, with more than one cell.

Organisms can be divided into groups. These include animals, plants, fungi and bacteria.

Cell types

Animal cells are surrounded by a cell membrane and contain a nucleus, ribosomes and mitochondria.

Plant cells are usually bigger than other cells and are surrounded by a cellulose cell wall with a membrane inside. They contain a nucleus and cytoplasm with a large central vacuole, ribosomes and mitochondria. Green plant cells also have chloroplasts.

Fungal cells are surrounded by a cell wall with a membrane inside and contain a vacuole, a nucleus, ribosomes and mitochondria.

Bacterial cells are usually very much smaller than other cells and are surrounded by a cell wall with a membrane inside. Their cytoplasm contains plasmids and ribosomes, but no organelles.

Cell structure

The fine structure of cells, which can only be seen using a high-magnification microscope, is called ultrastructure. Ultrastructure includes organelles such as nuclei, mitochondria and chloroplasts, which are specialised compartments found in most cells. Other ultrastructure features such as ribosomes and plasmids are not organelles.

Some structures, such as ribosomes, are found in cells from all types of organism. Figure 1.1 shows the general structure of different cells.

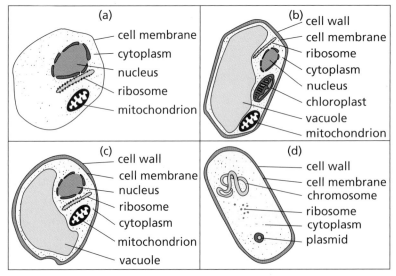

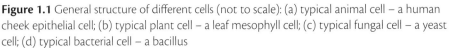

Figure 1.1 General structure of different cells (not to scale): (a) typical animal cell – a human cheek epithelial cell; (b) typical plant cell – a leaf mesophyll cell; (c) typical fungal cell – a yeast cell; (d) typical bacterial cell – a bacillus

Functions of cell structures

The different structures present in cells have different functions in the life of the cell. The different functions are shown in the table below and some of these are covered in other Key Areas, as indicated.

Cell structure	Function	Animal	Plant	Fungal	Bacterial
Nucleus	Contains genetic information (DNA) in animal, plant and fungal cells and so controls cell activities (see Key Areas 1.4 and 1.5 on pages 16 and 19)	✓	✓	✓	–
Plasmid	A small ring of genetic material in a bacterial cell	–	–	–	✓
Cell membrane	A selectively permeable membrane that controls entry and exit of substances such as O_2, CO_2, glucose and waste to and from all cells (see Key Area 1.2 on page 5)	✓	✓	✓	✓
Cytoplasm	Watery, jelly-like material within cells containing organelles that are the sites of various chemical reactions	✓	✓	✓	✓
Cell wall	The outer layer of plant, fungal and bacterial cells, which helps support the cell	–	✓	✓	✓
Vacuole	Membrane-bound sac that stores a solution of water, salts and sugars and helps support plant and fungal cells	–	✓	✓	–
Chloroplast	Makes carbohydrate in green plant cells using light energy in the process of photosynthesis (see Key Area 1.7 on page 27)	–	✓	–	–
Mitochondrion	Main site of ATP production in aerobic respiration in animal, plant and fungal cells (see Key Area 1.8 on page 32)	✓	✓	✓	–
Ribosome	Site of protein synthesis in cells (see Key Area 1.5 on page 19)	✓	✓	✓	✓

Note on cell walls

Cell walls are found in plant, fungal and bacterial cells. The walls of cells from these different groups of living organism differ in their structure and in the chemical substances of which they are made. Plant cell walls are composed of **cellulose**, whereas those of fungi and bacteria are varied in structure and chemical composition.

Hints & tips ⭐

Remember that the cell walls of different types of organism are similar but have different structures and chemical compositions.

Key words

Aerobic respiration – release of energy from food by a cell using oxygen

Bacterial cell – a tiny individual cell of a bacterium

Cell membrane – selectively permeable membrane enclosing the cell cytoplasm and controlling the entry and exit of materials

Cell wall – supports and prevents cells from bursting; plant, fungal and bacterial walls have different structures and chemical compositions

Cellulose – structural carbohydrate of which plant cell walls are composed

Chloroplast – organelle containing chlorophyll; the site of photosynthesis

Cytoplasm – jelly-like liquid containing cell organelles and the site of many chemical reactions

⇨

⇨
DNA – deoxyribonucleic acid; substance in chromosomes that carries the genetic code of an organism
Fungal cell – individual cell of a fungus
Mitochondrion – organelle that is the site of aerobic respiration and ATP production in cells
   (*pl.* mitochondria)
Multicellular – having many cells
Nucleus – organelle that is the control centre of a cell containing the genetic information of the organism
   (*pl.* nuclei)
Organelle – membrane-bound compartment with a specific function in animal, plant and fungal cells
Photosynthesis – process carried out by green plants to make their own food using light energy
Plasmid – circular genetic material present in bacterial cells and used in genetic engineering or modification
Protein – substance composed of chains of amino acids and containing the elements carbon, hydrogen, oxygen and nitrogen
Ribosome – site of protein synthesis
Ultrastructure – fine structure and detail of a cell and its organelles revealed by an electron microscope
Unicellular – single-celled
Vacuole – membrane-bound sac containing cell sap in plant and fungal cells

Questions ?

A Restricted-response questions (1 mark each)

1 Name **two** structures that are found in all cells.
2 Give **three** organelles found in animal, plant and fungal cells.
3 Name a structure found in bacterial cells only.
4 State how the cell walls of plant, fungal and bacterial cells vary.
5 State the function of mitochondria.
6 State why plant root cells cannot photosynthesise.
7 Give the function of a ribosome.

B Extended-response questions (2 or 3 marks each)

1 Explain why bacterial cells are difficult to study compared with plant cells.   (2)
2 Describe the structure and function of plant cell walls.   (2)
3 Describe the following cell structures:
   a) a plant cell vacuole
   b) a bacterial cell plasmid   (2)
4 Describe the similarities and differences in structure between a green plant cell and a bacterial cell.   (3)

Key Area 1.2
Transport across cell membranes

Key points ❗

1 The cell membrane is composed of **lipid** and protein. ☐

2 The cell membrane is **selectively permeable**. ☐

3 A difference in concentration of a substance is a **concentration gradient**. ☐

4 **Passive transport** of a substance does not require additional energy and describes the movement of its molecules down the concentration gradient from a high concentration to a lower concentration. ☐

5 **Diffusion** and **osmosis** are examples of passive transport processes. ☐

6 Diffusion is the movement of substances from a high concentration to a lower concentration down a concentration gradient. ☐

7 Examples of substances that enter most cells by diffusion are oxygen, glucose and amino acids. ☐

8 Examples of substances that leave most cells by diffusion are carbon dioxide and urea. ☐

9 Diffusion is important to cells because it helps provide the cell with raw materials and helps to remove waste products. ☐

10 Osmosis is the movement of water from a region of high water concentration to a region of lower water concentration through a selectively permeable membrane. ☐

11 An animal cell placed in a solution with a water concentration higher than that inside the cell will take up water by osmosis and could burst. ☐

12 An animal cell placed in a solution with a lower water concentration than that inside the cell will lose water by osmosis and could shrink. ☐

13 A plant cell placed in a solution with a water concentration higher than that inside the cell will take up water by osmosis and become **turgid**. ☐

14 A plant cell placed in a solution with a lower water concentration than that inside the cell will lose water by osmosis and become **plasmolysed**. ☐

15 Plasmolysed is the term used to describe a cell in which the vacuole has shrunk due to water loss, causing the cell membrane to pull away from the cell wall. ☐

16 Turgid is the term used to describe a cell or tissue in which the vacuole has swollen due to water gain and presses the cytoplasm and cell membrane against the cell wall. ☐

17 **Active transport** is the movement of molecules from a region of low concentration to a region of higher concentration, against the concentration gradient. ☐

18 Active transport requires additional energy (ATP) to allow membrane proteins to move molecules against the concentration gradient. ☐

Summary notes

Cell membrane structure

Cell membranes are at, or just inside, the boundaries of all cells. Membranes are extremely thin and are composed of protein and lipid molecules in a layered arrangement containing pores (Figure 1.2).

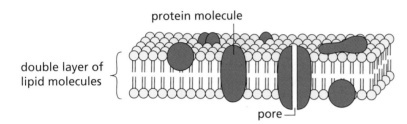

Figure 1.2 Structure of the cell membrane

Transport into and out of cells

The cells of a living organism exchange substances with each other and with their surroundings. This can happen in several ways including diffusion, osmosis and active transport. These terms all refer to the movement of molecules and involve concentration gradients, which are differences in concentration of these molecules between regions.

Diffusion and osmosis are passive because they do not require input of additional energy but active transport is active because of the additional energy it requires.

Diffusion

Diffusion is the passive movement of molecules from a region of high concentration to a region of lower concentration, which continues until they are evenly spread out. In living cells diffusion often occurs through membranes (Figure 1.3).

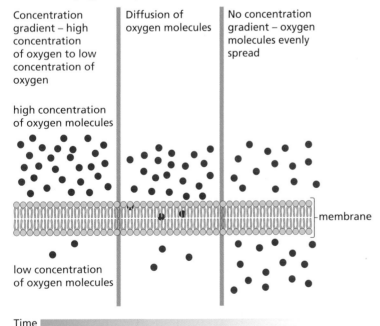

Figure 1.3 Diffusion of oxygen molecules through a cell membrane

A good example of diffusion in action is the exchange of gases in the lungs of a mammal. Oxygen molecules move from a region of high concentration in the lungs to a region of lower concentration in the red blood cells (Figure 1.4). Carbon dioxide moves by diffusion in the opposite direction. Diffusion is also the method of absorption of glucose and other foods through the small intestine of a mammal.

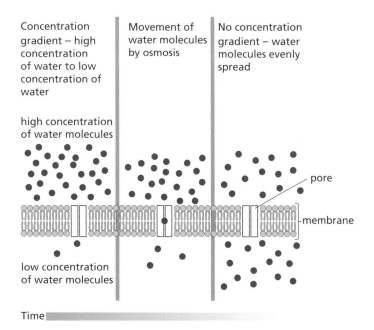

1 Breathes air with high concentration of oxygen molecules into lung spaces
2 Oxygen molecules diffuse from high concentration in lung spaces to lower concentration in the blood
3 Blood transported to cells of body
4 Oxygen molecules diffuse from high concentration in blood to lower concentration in body cells

Figure 1.4 Diffusion of oxygen in the body of a mammal

Osmosis

Osmosis is a special case of diffusion. It is the passive movement of water molecules from a region of high water concentration to a region of lower water concentration. Water movement by osmosis is always through a selectively permeable membrane (Figure 1.5).

Concentration gradient – high concentration of water to low concentration of water

Movement of water molecules by osmosis

No concentration gradient – water molecules evenly spread

high concentration of water molecules

pore

membrane

low concentration of water molecules

Time

Figure 1.5 Osmosis

A good example of osmosis in action is the uptake of water into the root cells of plants. When the soil is moist after rain, the soil water concentration is higher than that of plant root cells. Water therefore passes from high concentration in the soil to lower concentration in the root cells by osmosis. There is more about osmosis in plant roots in Key Area 2.6a.

Active transport

Active transport is the movement of molecules from a region of low concentration to a region of higher concentration against a concentration gradient. Active transport requires energy.

In some cases it is essential that cells with high concentration of a substance receive more of that substance from areas where the substance is at a lower concentration. A good example of this is found in certain unicellular freshwater plants such as *Nitella*. The cells of this plant require potassium ions from their environment to survive. However, potassium ion concentrations in freshwater are very low. *Nitella* cells use energy from their respiration process to take up potassium ions from low concentrations in freshwater to the higher concentrations that must be maintained in their cells. The energy goes to the cell membrane proteins, which carry the ions through the membranes from outside to inside (Figure 1.6).

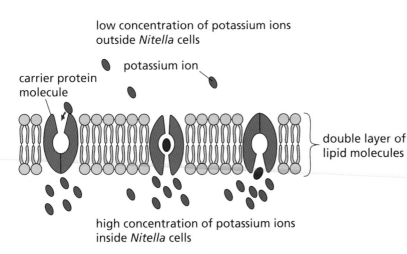

Figure 1.6 Active transport of potassium ions in *Nitella*

Another example of active transport involves the movement of potassium and sodium ions through the membranes of nerve cells.

Active transport in nerve cells

To function normally nerve cells need to maintain high concentrations of potassium ions inside and high concentrations of sodium ions outside the cells. To do this, their membranes have special proteins called sodium-potassium pumps. These proteins use energy to pump sodium ions out of the cell and pump potassium ions in (Figure 1.7). The energy source is a substance called ATP, which is formed using energy released during respiration. Details of respiration are in Key Area 1.8 and there is more about nerve cells in Key Area 2.3a.

⇨

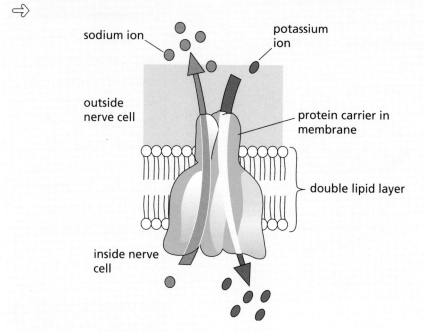

Figure 1.7 Sodium-potassium pump in nerve cells

Animal cells and water

The results of placing animal cells in solutions of different water concentration can be shown using red blood cells (Figure 1.8). If animal cells are placed in a solution with a water concentration higher than the cell contents, water is taken in by osmosis and the cells might burst. If placed in a solution of lower water concentration than the cell contents, water will be lost by osmosis and the cell will shrink.

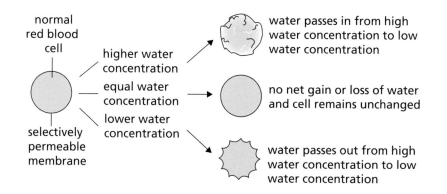

Figure 1.8 Effects of water on a red blood cell

Plant cells and water

The results of placing plant cells in solutions of different water concentration are shown in Figure 1.9. If plants cells are immersed in a solution with a water concentration higher than the cell contents, they will take up water by osmosis and their vacuoles will fill. Further intake of water is prevented because vacuole size is limited by the presence of the cell wall. Plant cells that have full vacuoles are said to be turgid, the normal state for a plant cell. Plant cells immersed in a solution with a lower water concentration than the cell contents lose water by osmosis and their vacuoles shrink and eventually pull the cell membrane and cytoplasm away from the cell walls of the cell. This is not desirable for the plant and may actually kill it. Cells with membranes pulled away from their walls are said to be plasmolysed.

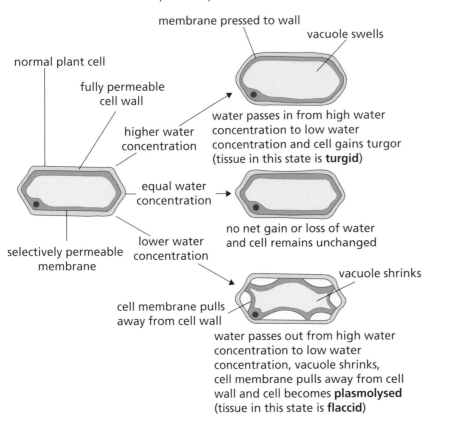

Figure 1.9 Effects of water on a plant cell

Key words

Active transport – transport of molecules against their concentration gradient

Concentration gradient – difference in concentration between two solutions, cells or solutions and cells

Diffusion – passive movement of molecules from an area of high concentration to an area of lower concentration

Lipid – fat or oil with molecules composed of fatty acids and glycerol

Osmosis – movement of water molecules from an area of high to an area of lower water concentration through a selectively permeable membrane

Passive transport – movement of molecules without the need for additional energy, e.g. diffusion and osmosis

Plasmolysed – description of a plant cell in which the vacuole has shrunk and the membrane has pulled away from the wall due to water loss

Selectively permeable – refers to a membrane that controls the movement of certain molecules depending on their size

Turgid – description of a swollen plant cell with a full vacuole resulting from water intake due to osmosis

Questions ?

A Restricted-response questions (1 mark each)

1 Name **two** substances present in cell membranes.
2 Give **two** passive processes by which substances pass through membranes.
3 State the difference between an active and a passive process.
4 State **one** difference between osmosis and diffusion.
5 Give the meanings of the following terms:
   a) turgid
   b) plasmolysed
6 Give an example of a situation in which cells use active transport.
7 State what is meant by a concentration gradient.

B Extended-response questions (2 or 3 marks)

1 Describe the process of diffusion.   (2)
2 Describe the role of protein molecules in osmosis and in active transport. (2)
3 Explain what would happen to a piece of potato tissue placed into a beaker of pure water
  for 2 hours.   (3)
4 Explain why immersing a single animal cell in sea water might kill it.   (3)

Key Area 1.3
Producing new cells

Key points ❗

1 The nucleus of a cell contains genetic information (DNA) organised into **chromosomes**. ☐
2 The **chromosome complement** of a cell is the number and type of chromosomes it contains. ☐
3 The chromosome complement of most cells is **diploid**, which means that their nuclei have two matching sets of chromosomes. ☐
4 The nucleus controls cell activities including **mitosis**. ☐
5 **Replication** is the process by which DNA copies itself. ☐
6 During mitosis, each chromosome is replicated. ☐
7 A replicated chromosome is called a **chromatid**. ☐
8 In mitosis the nucleus of a diploid parent cell divides to produce two diploid nuclei. ☐
9 Daughter cells are genetically identical to their parent cell. ☐
10 The sequence of events in mitosis starts with chromosomes replicating and becoming visible as pairs of chromatids. The chromosomes line up at the **equator** and their chromatids are pulled to opposite **poles** by **spindle fibres** to form two new nuclei. ☐
11 After mitosis, the cell cytoplasm splits between the new nuclei to form two daughter cells. ☐
12 Cells can be induced to undergo mitosis and cell division artificially in cell culture. ☐
13 Cell culture requires aseptic techniques, in which growth of other cells such as bacteria is prevented and the culture remains uncontaminated. ☐
14 Cell culture requires an appropriate liquid or solid medium such as nutrient agars or broths in which the cells can grow and divide. ☐
15 In cell culture, factors such as temperature, pH and oxygen levels are controlled. ☐

Summary notes

Chromosomes

A human being is an example of a living organism whose body is made up from cells. The nucleus of most cells contains two matching sets of chromosomes. Each set has been copied from one of the individual's parents. A cell with two matching sets of chromosomes is said to be diploid. The diploid number in humans is 46. Each chromosome has a group of inherited units called **genes** packaged into it. Genes are composed of a substance called deoxyribonucleic acid (**DNA**). DNA has the genetic information of the cell coded into its large, complex molecules.

Hints & tips ⭐

Use this diamond idea to remember how genetic information is organised.

DNA
Gene
Chromosome
Nucleus
Cell

The table below summarises this information.

Term	Meaning
Nucleus	Organelle in a cell containing the diploid chromosome complement
Chromosome	Structure in which genetic information is packaged
Gene	Unit of genetic information found on a chromosome
Deoxyribonucleic acid (DNA)	Substance of which genes are composed and into which genetic information is coded

Mitosis and cell division

Living organisms grow by producing new cells. New cells are produced when the nuclei of parent cells divide by mitosis and their cytoplasm is split into two. Before mitosis, the DNA of a parent cell is copied exactly in a process called replication. Following replication each chromosome appears as a double structure made up of two chromatids – each chromatid is a replicated chromosome. During mitosis, a fibrous structure called the spindle appears in the dividing cell and the chromatids are pulled apart by its fibres.

Figure 1.10 shows a cell with a diploid number of four undergoing mitosis and cytoplasm splitting. Each daughter cell is identical to the parent cell because it has an exact copy of the parent cell's genetic information.

Cell with diploid number of four

Chromosomes replicate and spindles appear

Chromosomes move to equator

Chromatids pulled apart

Nuclear membranes reform and cytoplasm splits to form two daughter cells

Figure 1.10 Stages of mitosis in a cell with a diploid number of four

Importance of mitosis

Mitosis is important because it ensures that each daughter cell contains a chromatid from each of the parent cell chromosomes. This means that each daughter cell will be genetically identical to the parent cell and contain all the genetic information needed to carry out all of its activities and functions. Mitosis ensures that cells of an individual organism are genetically identical to each other.

Cell culture

It is useful for humans to be able to produce many copies of a specific cell by encouraging cells to undergo mitosis and division in a pure culture. Culturing yeasts for brewing and baking industries and bacteria for dairy industries are good examples. Cell culture can be important in medicine

Hints & tips

Try using eight pieces of a drinking straw or wool and some sticky tape to make four model chromosomes – use them to practise the chromosome movements in mitosis.

to create pure cultures of human cells that can be used experimentally without risks to human subjects.

It is essential to use aseptic techniques when working with cultures to avoid contamination by unwanted cells, especially foreign bacteria. Contaminated cultures are useless and might be dangerous. Figure 1.11 summarises an aseptic technique.

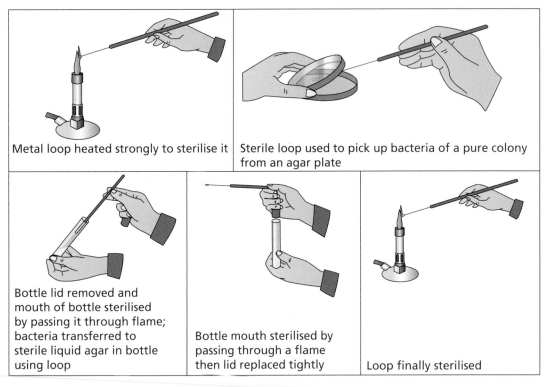

Metal loop heated strongly to sterilise it	Sterile loop used to pick up bacteria of a pure colony from an agar plate

Bottle lid removed and mouth of bottle sterilised by passing it through flame; bacteria transferred to sterile liquid agar in bottle using loop

Bottle mouth sterilised by passing through a flame then lid replaced tightly

Loop finally sterilised

Figure 1.11 An aseptic technique; in this example a pure sample of a species of bacterium is taken from a dish and added to a bottle

Various factors such as temperature, pH and oxygen levels are controlled in cell cultures so that optimum conditions for mitosis and cell division are achieved. Mitosis, like all cell activities, is dependent on enzymes, so factors that affect enzymes, such as temperature and pH, also affect mitosis. Respiration produces energy for mitosis and so food molecules must be present in the growth medium and oxygen availability must also be controlled.

Key words

Aseptic techniques – laboratory procedures designed to prevent contamination of pure cultures of microorganisms

Chromatid – replicated copy of a chromosome visible during cell division

Chromosome complement – the characteristic number of chromosomes in a typical cell of an organism

Chromosome – structure containing hereditary material; composed of DNA that codes for all the characteristics of an organism

Diploid – describes a cell containing two sets of chromosomes

Equator – middle position in a cell where chromosomes attach to the spindle during mitosis

Medium – solid or liquid nutrient agar or broth used to culture microorganisms

$\Rightarrow$

⇨

Mitosis – division of the nucleus of a cell that leads to the production of two genetically identical diploid daughter cells

Poles – opposite ends of a cell to which chromatids migrate during mitosis

Replication – copying of DNA to produce chromatids before mitosis

Spindle fibres – protein threads produced during mitosis to pull chromatids apart

Questions ?

A Restricted-response questions (1 mark each)

1 Give the term used to describe a cell containing two matching sets of chromosomes.
2 Give the term applied to replicated chromosomes before they separate during mitosis.
3 State the role of the spindle fibres during mitosis.
4 Give the function of a growth medium for bacteria.

B Extended-response questions (2 or 3 marks)

1 Describe what happens to the chromosomes of a cell before mitosis takes place. (2)
2 Give the correct sequence for the following steps in mitosis from the start of the process.
   a) Chromatids separate to the spindle poles.
   b) Chromosomes become visible as double strands.
   c) Two new nuclei form.
   d) Chromosomes line up at the equator of the spindle. (2)
3 Explain the importance of maintaining the diploid chromosome number following mitosis. (2)
4 Explain why cell culture methods need aseptic techniques. (2)
5 Explain why temperature and pH must be controlled during the cell culture process. (2)
6 Explain the importance of mitosis to multicellular organisms. (3)

Key Area 1.4
DNA and the production of proteins

Key points (!)

1 The nucleus of living cells contains genetic information organised into chromosomes. ☐
2 Chromosomes are made up of regions called genes. ☐
3 DNA is a complex substance that forms the genes of all living organisms. ☐
4 DNA carries the genetic information, which is information for making proteins. ☐
5 A single DNA molecule is a **double-stranded helix**. ☐
6 Each strand of DNA is a chain carrying molecules called **bases**. ☐
7 There are four different types of base known as **Adenine (A)**, **Thymine (T)**, **Guanine (G)** and **Cytosine (C)**. ☐
8 The strands of the DNA helix are held by **bonds** between bases on each strand. ☐
9 The bases bond together to form **complementary** base pairs. ☐
10 Base A only pairs with T and base G only pairs with C. ☐
11 The sequence of bases A, T, G and C make up the **genetic code**. ☐
12 The base sequence of a specific gene determines the **amino acid** sequence in the specific protein to be assembled. ☐
13 Proteins are assembled at ribosomes in the cell cytoplasm. ☐
14 **Messenger RNA (mRNA)** is a molecule that carries a complementary copy of the code from the DNA in the nucleus to a ribosome. ☐

Summary notes
Structure of DNA

Genes are made from deoxyribonucleic acid (DNA) molecules. DNA is a substance with large, complex molecules. These molecules carry the genetic information of a cell coded into them. Each DNA molecule is in the shape of a double-stranded helix, as shown in Figure 1.12. Each strand carries chemical units called bases of which there are four different types. The bases are known by the upper-case first letters of their chemical names – **A**denine, **T**hymine, **G**uanine and **C**ytosine.

The two strands are held together by bonds between bases on each strand. A on one strand always pairs with T on the other strand and G on one strand always pairs with C on the other strand. These bases are said to be complementary to each other – A with T and G with C. Figure 1.13 shows details of the complementary base pairing in DNA.

Hints & tips ⭐

*It is worth concentrating on the word **complementary**. It means a perfect match – like a hand in a glove.*

Genetic code

A cell's genetic code allows the cell to make the specific proteins it needs. Each gene has a code for a different protein. Different species have different genes and so are able to make different proteins.

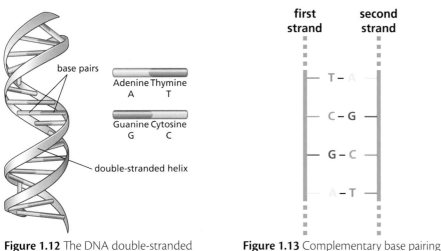

Figure 1.12 The DNA double-stranded helix – note how the two strands are linked by pairs of bases

Figure 1.13 Complementary base pairing

Each type of protein is made up from a chain of amino acids in an order set by the genetic code. It is the sequence of bases along one strand of a DNA molecule that encodes its genetic information.

There are 20 different amino acids that occur naturally. Organisms obtain amino acids from their diet and transport them to each of their cells.

Protein synthesis

DNA is found in the nucleus of a cell while proteins are assembled from amino acids at the ribosomes found in the cytoplasm. A complementary copy of the code from the DNA in the nucleus is carried to a ribosome by a messenger RNA (mRNA) molecule. mRNA has the base **U**racil in place of **T**hymine. Figure 1.14 shows a DNA code being copied as a complementary copy to mRNA and then carried to a ribosome to be translated into a protein molecule.

Hints & tips

Remember: order of DNA bases → order of mRNA bases → order of amino acids in protein

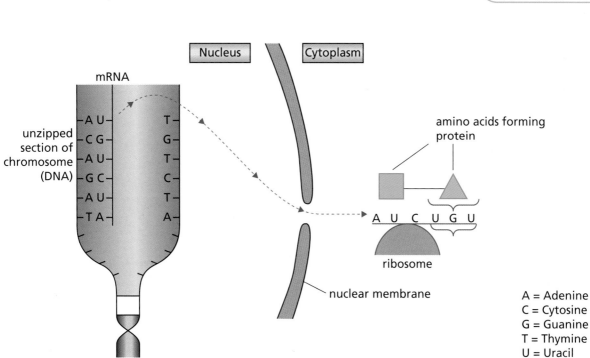

Figure 1.14 Protein synthesis

A = Adenine
C = Cytosine
G = Guanine
T = Thymine
U = Uracil

17

Key words

A, G, T, C and U – letters that represent the names of bases of DNA and mRNA (Adenine, Guanine, Thymine, Cytosine and Uracil)
Amino acid – a building block of a protein molecule
Bases – form the genetic code of DNA and mRNA
Bond – chemical link between atoms in a molecule
Complementary – fitting together like a hand in a glove; applied to DNA base pairing
Double-stranded helix – describes the spiral ladder shape of DNA molecules
Gene – small section of DNA that codes for the production of a specific protein
Genetic code – code formed by the sequence of the bases in DNA that determines an organism's characteristics
Messenger RNA (mRNA) – substance that carries a complementary copy of the genetic code from DNA to the ribosomes

Questions ?

A Restricted-response questions (1 mark each)

1 State the role of DNA in cells.
2 State what is meant by the term genetic information.
3 Describe the overall shape of a DNA molecule.
4 Give the letters by which the four bases that make up the genetic code in a DNA molecule are known.
5 Give the pairs of letters of the complementary bases in DNA.
6 Give the term that refers to a section of DNA with a specific sequence of bases that code for the production of a specific protein.
7 Name the molecule that carries a complementary copy of the base sequence of DNA out of the nucleus.
8 State the location within a cell where amino acids are assembled to produce protein molecules.

B Extended-response questions (2 or 3 marks)

1 Explain the term complementary in relation to base pairs in a molecule of DNA. (2)
2 Describe the feature of an mRNA molecule that ensures the order of the amino acids in a protein is correct. (2)
3 Describe the role of mRNA in the process of protein synthesis. (3)

Key Area 1.5
Proteins and enzymes

Key points !

1 The variety of protein shapes arises from the sequence of amino acids in their molecules. ☐
2 The shape of protein molecules affects their function. ☐
3 The functions of proteins include **structural**, **enzymes**, **hormones**, **antibodies** and **receptors**. ☐
4 Structural proteins make up cell structures such as membranes. ☐
5 Enzymes function as biological **catalysts** and are made by all living cells. ☐
6 Hormones act as chemical messengers between cells and travel in body fluids such as blood. ☐
7 Antibodies are protein molecules that are involved in body defences. ☐
8 Receptors are found in cell membranes and recognise specific substances. ☐
9 Enzymes speed up cellular reactions and are unchanged in the process. ☐
10 The substance upon which an enzyme acts is called its **substrate**. ☐
11 Enzyme molecules have **active sites** where they bind to substrate molecules. ☐
12 Enzymes are **specific** because the shape of the active site of each enzyme molecule is **complementary** to the shape of its substrate. ☐
13 Each type of enzyme works best in its **optimum** conditions. ☐
14 Enzymes and other proteins are affected by temperature and pH. ☐
15 Extremes of temperature or pH can result in changes to the molecular shapes of enzymes known as **denaturation**. ☐
16 A change in the molecular shape of an enzyme will affect its rate of reaction. ☐
17 A change in the molecular shape of any protein molecule will affect its function. ☐

Summary notes

Variety of proteins

There is a huge variety of different proteins with different functions that are found in living organisms. The variety of shapes and functions arises from the different sequences of amino acids each protein has.

Functions of proteins

The functions of proteins can be grouped as shown in the table below.

Protein group	Function	Example
Structural units	Give strength and support to cellular structures	Membrane proteins give membranes their shape and strength
Enzymes	Act as biological catalysts to speed up chemical reactions in cells	Amylase speeds up the breakdown of starch molecules in animal digestive systems
Hormones	Carry specific messages in the bloodstream of living organisms	Insulin signals to the mammal liver to store excess glucose
Antibodies	Provide specific defence against body invaders such as certain bacteria and viruses	Immunoglobulins give specific defence against invading influenza viruses
Receptors	Allow cells to recognise specific substances	Liver cells have receptors for insulin

Enzymes

Enzymes act as biological catalysts to speed up chemical reactions in cells, which would otherwise proceed too slowly to maintain life. The general action of enzymes is shown in Figure 1.15.

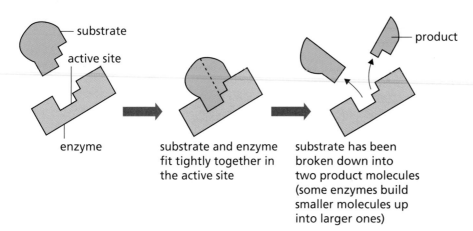

Figure 1.15 Enzyme action

The substance that a particular enzyme works on is called its substrate and those substances made are **products**. Enzyme molecules have a region of their surface known as the active site. The active site is complementary in shape to the substrate molecules and binds to them specifically – each enzyme has its own specific substrate.

Different enzymes are responsible for different reactions because the substrates they work on differ in shape. Enzyme molecules are unchanged by their activity, so each enzyme molecule can catalyse a chemical reaction and then be used again.

Enzymes and temperature

Enzyme activity is affected by the temperature of its environment. Warmer conditions cause enzyme and substrate molecules to move around faster and so meet more regularly, resulting in increased rates of reaction. However, at higher temperatures enzyme molecules might become denatured. This process changes the shape of the active site and stops the denatured enzyme from working altogether. As shown in Figure 1.16, an enzyme has an optimum temperature at which it works best.

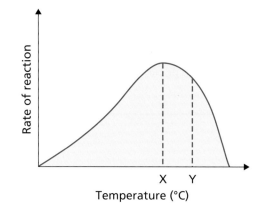

X is the optimum temperature for this reaction

At Y the higher temperature has started to denature the enzyme molecules, reducing the rate of reaction

Figure 1.16 The effect of temperature on enzyme action

Enzymes and pH

Enzyme activity is also affected by pH. Each enzyme has a pH at which it works best, but slight changes in the pH can result in changes to the active site, which will stop the enzyme working altogether (Figure 1.17).

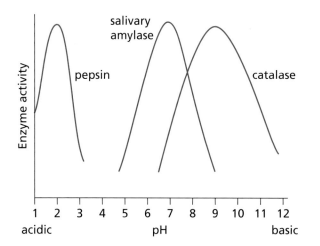
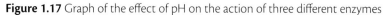

Figure 1.17 Graph of the effect of pH on the action of three different enzymes

Key words

Active site – position on the surface of an enzyme molecule to which specific substrate molecules can bind

Antibody – protein that is involved in defence in animals

Catalyst – a substance that speeds up a chemical reaction by reducing the energy required to start it

Denaturation – change in the shape of molecules of protein such as enzymes, resulting in them becoming non-functional

Enzyme – protein produced by living cells that acts as a biological catalyst

Hormone – protein released by an endocrine gland into the blood to act as a chemical messenger

Optimum – conditions such as temperature and pH at which an enzyme works best

Product – substance made by an enzyme-catalysed reaction

Receptor – cell surface protein which allows a cell to recognise specific substances

Specific – each different enzyme acts on one substrate only

Structural – referring to the proteins in membranes, muscle, bone, hair, nails etc.

Substrate – the substance on which an enzyme works

Questions ?

A Restricted-response questions (1 mark each)

1 State the feature of a protein that determines its molecular shape and the function it can carry out.
2 Give **four** protein groups that have different functions.
3 State why enzymes are described as biological catalysts.
4 State the effects of catalysing a reaction on an enzyme molecule's structure.
5 State why living cells require enzymes.
6 Give the term used for the substance on which an enzyme works.
7 Name the part of an enzyme molecule that binds to its substrate.
8 Give **two** different conditions that could lead to the denaturing of enzyme molecules.

B Extended-response question (2 or 3 marks)

1 Explain the following terms as they are applied to enzymes.
   a) specific
   b) optimum   (2)
2 Describe what happens to an enzyme molecule's structure and function when it becomes denatured. (2)
3 Describe the main characteristics of enzymes.   (3)

Key Area 1.6
Genetic engineering

Key points !

1 Normal control of bacterial cell activity depends on genetic information. ☐
2 Genetic information can be transferred from the cells of one species to the cells of another naturally or artificially. ☐
3 Natural methods of transfer include fertilisation in animals and plants and transfer of plasmids between bacterial species or by **viruses**. ☐
4 Artificial transfer of genetic information is called **genetic engineering**. ☐
5 Genetic engineering often, but not always, involves bacteria. ☐
6 Pieces of chromosome can be transferred from a **donor** species to another, which then allows the **recipient** species to make new proteins. ☐
7 Genetic engineering is carried out by humans to allow a species to make a protein that is normally made by another species. ☐
8 Stages of genetic engineering include identifying a section of DNA that contains the required gene from the chromosomes of a donor species and extracting it, inserting the required gene into a **vector** or bacterial plasmid, then **transforming** the recipient (host) cell by placing the modified plasmid into it. ☐
9 Following genetic engineering, transformed cells are cultured to produce a **GM (genetically modified)** strain or organism. ☐
10 The GM strain or organism can produce a new protein normally made by another species. ☐

Summary notes
Genetic engineering

Genetic information can be transferred from one cell to another naturally. This is the basis of sexual reproduction in which the genetic information from a sperm cell is transferred to an egg cell during fertilisation.

Some bacterial species can transfer plasmids between them naturally. Viruses carry genetic material into the cells of other species.

In recent decades, scientists have discovered that genetic material can be transferred artificially from cells of one species to the cells of another completely different species using techniques called genetic engineering. Human genes have been transferred to bacteria so that the fast-growing and rapidly reproducing bacteria make human proteins that are required medically. One example involves locating the gene that codes for the protein insulin on a human chromosome and then transferring it to a bacterial species that can be cultured rapidly to produce the large amounts of insulin required to treat an ever-increasing number of diabetics. Figure 1.18 shows the steps in this process. There is more about diabetes in Key Area 2.3b.

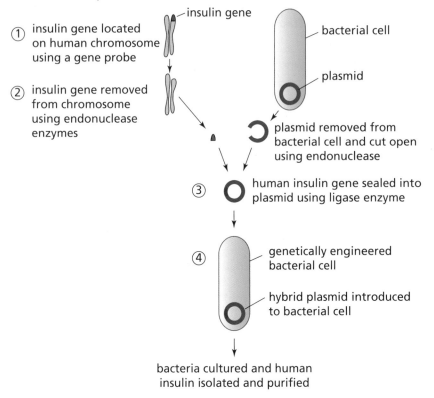

① insulin gene located on human chromosome using a gene probe

② insulin gene removed from chromosome using endonuclease enzymes

insulin gene

bacterial cell

plasmid

plasmid removed from bacterial cell and cut open using endonuclease

③ human insulin gene sealed into plasmid using ligase enzyme

④ genetically engineered bacterial cell

hybrid plasmid introduced to bacterial cell

bacteria cultured and human insulin isolated and purified

Figure 1.18 Steps in genetic engineering

Genetically modified (GM) organisms

In more recent times the transfer of genetic material from one organism to another has been applied more widely. Genes have been taken from a wide variety of organisms and used to transform cells of crop plants to improve yield. These are genetically modified (GM) crops. The table below shows some of the modifications that have been developed in crop plants in recent years.

Crop plant	Genetic modification and advantage
Rice	Genes from daffodil and soil bacteria allow the rice plant to produce vitamin A in its seeds
Rapeseed	Genes from other organisms that give the crop herbicide resistance allow herbicides to be used to kill weeds among the crop, so increasing yield
Tomato	Soil bacteria carry genes from other bacteria that code for an insecticide protein into tomato cells, so increasing yield
Potato	Genes from other organisms give potato plants fungal resistance, so increasing yield

Research is continuing into the use of artificial genes that can be engineered into domestic chickens to give them protection against bird flu.

GM organisms offer the potential for great benefits to humans but there are also issues connected to their production and use.

Benefits and issues with GM organisms

Information about the potential benefits of producing GM organisms is in Key Area 3.5. This emphasises how GM organisms could help to reduce the impact of intensive farming on the environment. However, there are also issues that the use of GM organisms has raised, and this has confirmed the need for caution in their use. Some of the benefits and issues are summarised below.

Hints & tips

Remember that transfer of genetic material happens naturally as well as artificially — make sure you know examples of both.

Benefits:

● GM crops and animals can be higher yielding and better tasting.
● They can increase food security for increasing human populations.
● They can have a positive impact on the environment through the potential for decreasing pesticide use.
● They can potentially play a part in the conservation of soil, water and energy.

Issues:

● There are safety issues related to human health.
● Environmental issues are caused by the potential for unintended release of genes into wild populations.
● There is concern over domination of food production by GM companies in industrial countries.
● Ethical issues related to tampering with nature are raised.
● There is concern that we simply do not know, or understand, the potential problems.

Key words

Donor – organism from which the genetic material is obtained for transfer to another species
Genetic engineering – the artificial transfer of genetic information from one donor cell or organism to another
Recipient – a cell or organism that receives genetic material from a donor cell or organism
Transforming – modification of an organism genetically by genetic engineering
Vector – method of transferring genetic material from a donor to a recipient, e.g. viruses, bacterial cells or plasmids
Virus – microorganism that can be used in the transfer of genetic information

Questions ?

A Restricted-response questions (1 mark each)

1 State **one** way in which DNA can be transferred naturally between species.
2 Give the term applied to the transfer of DNA artificially between cells.
3 Give the terms used to describe species that supply and receive genetic material by genetic engineering.

⇨

⇨
4   Give the meaning of the term vector.
5   Give the meaning of the term transformed cell.
6   Give the meaning of the term GM organism.
7   Name one human hormone produced by genetic engineering.

B Extended-response question (2 or 3 marks)

1   Arrange the following steps in a genetic engineering process into the correct order.
    a) insert modified plasmid into host cell
    b) extract the required gene
    c) insert required gene into bacterial plasmid
    d) identify DNA of required gene on donor chromosome   (2)
2   Explain why bacteria are suitable organisms to use in genetic engineering.   (2)
3   Describe why some people have concerns about the use of genetic engineering in the production
    of GM organisms.   (3)
4   Genetic engineering often uses bacteria to produce the human hormone, insulin. Outline the stages
    involved in this process.   (3)

Key Area 1.7
Photosynthesis

Key points ❗

1 Photosynthesis is the chemical process by which green plants make **carbohydrate**. ☐
2 Photosynthesis is a series of enzyme-controlled reactions in two stages. ☐
3 The first stage of photosynthesis is the **light-dependent stage**. ☐
4 In the light-dependent stage, light energy from the sun is trapped by **chlorophyll** in the chloroplasts and is converted into chemical energy in molecules of **ATP**. ☐
5 In the light-dependent stage, water molecules are split to produce hydrogen and oxygen. Excess oxygen diffuses from chloroplasts and out of the cell. ☐
6 The second stage of photosynthesis is the **carbon fixation stage**. ☐
7 In the carbon fixation stage, hydrogen from the light-dependent stage is combined with carbon dioxide to produce **sugar**. ☐
8 In the carbon fixation stage, energy from ATP is used in the production of sugar. ☐
9 The chemical energy in sugar can be released during respiration. ☐
10 Sugar not used in respiration can be converted to plant products such as **starch** or **cellulose**. ☐
11 Starch acts as a store of energy in plants while cellulose is a main chemical component of plant cell walls. ☐
12 A **limiting factor** is a variable that, when in short supply, can limit the rate of a chemical reaction such as photosynthesis. ☐
13 The rate of photosynthesis is limited by various factors such as temperature, light intensity and the concentration of carbon dioxide available. ☐

Summary notes

Equation for photosynthesis

Photosynthesis is the process by which green plants make their own food. Carbon dioxide from the air and water from the soil are combined in green cells in the presence of light energy to produce sugar (glucose) and oxygen. This can be summarised by the following equation:

$$\text{water} + \text{carbon dioxide} \xrightarrow[\text{chlorophyll}]{\text{light}} \text{sugar (glucose)} + \text{oxygen}$$

Photosynthesis: a two-stage process

Photosynthesis is an example of an enzyme-controlled process in cells. It is a two-stage process.

First stage: light reactions

The first stage of photosynthesis is light dependent. Light energy from the sun is trapped by pigment molecules such as chlorophyll in the chloroplasts of green plants. The energy is then converted to chemical energy stored in molecules of adenosine triphosphate (ATP), which are passed to the second stage.

In the same set of reactions, water molecules are split into hydrogen and oxygen molecules. The hydrogen is passed to the second stage but the oxygen diffuses from cells and is eventually released from the plant into the atmosphere.

Second stage: carbon fixation

The second stage of photosynthesis is completely temperature dependent because of the enzymes involved. ATP and hydrogen from the first stage are used with carbon dioxide that has been taken from the environment to produce sugar (glucose), which contains the chemical energy. This chemical energy is available for respiration, or the sugar can be converted to plant products such as starch, cellulose, lipids and proteins.

The stages of photosynthesis are shown in Figure 1.19.

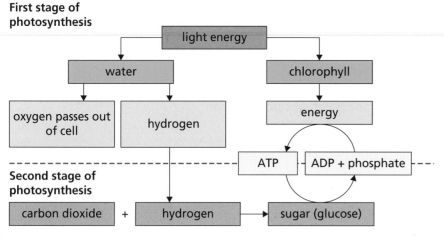

Figure 1.19 Two stages of photosynthesis

Investigating photosynthesis
Conditions for photosynthesis

A green plant leaf kept in the dark will become de-starched because it uses its starch up to provide it with energy when not photosynthesising. Leaves can be tested for starch using **iodine solution**, which turns from brown to blue-black with starch (Figure 1.20).

Step 1: Boil leaf in water then in alcohol

Step 2: Place leaf on tile then flood with iodine solution

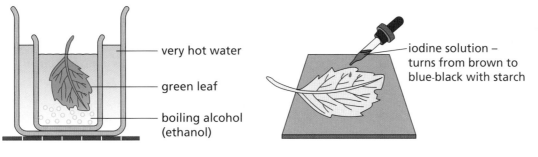

- very hot water
- green leaf
- boiling alcohol (ethanol)

iodine solution – turns from brown to blue-black with starch

Figure 1.20 Testing a leaf for starch

A de-starched plant can be used to confirm factors needed for photosynthesis (Figure 1.21).

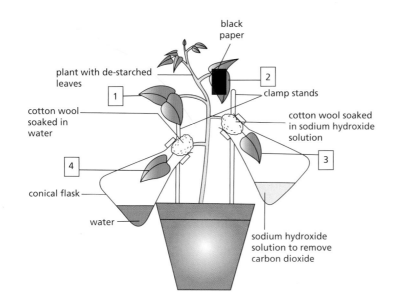

black paper

plant with de-starched leaves

cotton wool soaked in water

conical flask

water

clamp stands

cotton wool soaked in sodium hydroxide solution

sodium hydroxide solution to remove carbon dioxide

1

2

3

4

Figure 1.21 Investigating requirements for photosynthesis

Presence of starch in the leaves indicates that photosynthesis has occurred. The table below shows results of starch tests on the experimental leaves in Figure 1.21.

Leaf	Conditions given	Iodine test	Conclusion
1	Light and CO_2	Starch present	Photosynthesis has occurred
2	No light, CO_2	Starch absent	Photosynthesis requires light
3	Light, no CO_2	Starch absent	Photosynthesis requires CO_2
4	Light and CO_2 (control for leaf 3)	Starch present	Presence of flask for leaf 3 does not affect photosynthesis

Rate of photosynthesis

The rate of photosynthesis can be investigated using stems of aquatic plants such as *Cabomba*. Figure 1.22 shows an experimental set-up used in this type of investigation. Oxygen is a product of photosynthesis so its rate of production can be used as a measure of the rate of photosynthesis.

Hints & tips

Production of starch is often used to indicate that photosynthesis has occurred – make sure you know the test for starch shown in Figure 1.20.

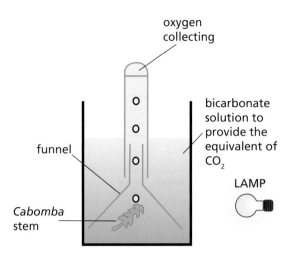

oxygen collecting

bicarbonate solution to provide the equivalent of CO_2

funnel

LAMP

Cabomba stem

Figure 1.22 *Cabomba* bubbler

Limiting factors

The rate of chemical reactions such as photosynthesis can be limited by factors that are at low levels or are in short supply. Low temperature or light intensity can limit the rate of photosynthesis. The concentration of carbon dioxide available to the plant can also be limiting.

The graph in Figure 1.23 shows the effects of various combinations of temperature and carbon dioxide concentration on the rate of photosynthesis. Note how the graphs are very similar in shape.

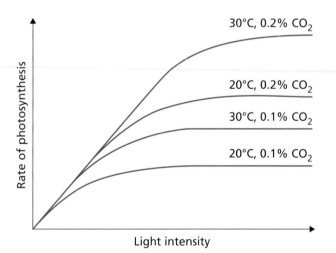

30°C, 0.2% CO_2

20°C, 0.2% CO_2

30°C, 0.1% CO_2

20°C, 0.1% CO_2

Rate of photosynthesis

Light intensity

Figure 1.23 Effects of limiting factors on the rate of photosynthesis

> **Hints & tips**
>
> Measuring the **rate** of photosynthesis always requires a measurement of **time** to be made – bubbles of oxygen **per minute**.

> **Hints & tips**
>
> On limiting factor graphs, watch for the slope of the line – if the line slopes, then the factor on the x-axis is limiting the rate; where the line is level, some other factor is limiting the rate.

> **Hints & tips**
>
> It is better to write about light **energy** or light **intensity** rather than simply using the word light.

Key words

ATP – adenosine triphosphate; a substance that transfers chemical energy in cells

Carbohydrate – a substance such as sugar, starch or glycogen, containing the elements carbon, hydrogen and oxygen

Carbon fixation stage – second stage in photosynthesis in which ATP, hydrogen and carbon dioxide are involved in the production of sugar

Chlorophyll – green pigment in chloroplasts that absorbs light energy for the process of photosynthesis

Iodine solution – brown-coloured solution that turns blue-black with starch

Light-dependent stage – first stage in photosynthesis producing hydrogen and ATP required in the carbon fixation stage

⇨

⇨

Limiting factor – a variable that, when in short supply, can limit the rate of a chemical reaction such as photosynthesis

Starch – storage carbohydrate in plants

Sugar – energy-rich sub-units made by green plants in photosynthesis that can join into larger carbohydrates such as starch

Questions ❓

A Restricted-response questions (1 mark each)

1 Name the two stages of photosynthesis.
2 Name the pigment in chloroplasts that traps the light energy required for photosynthesis.
3 In the light-dependent stage of photosynthesis light energy is converted to chemical energy. Name the molecule in which the chemical energy is stored.
4 In the light-dependent stage, some energy is used to split water molecules. State what happens to the oxygen and hydrogen produced by this split.
5 State the role of carbon dioxide in the carbon fixation stage of photosynthesis.
6 Give **three** possible limiting factors in the process of photosynthesis.

B Extended-response questions (2 or 3 marks)

1 Write the word equation for photosynthesis. (2)
2 Describe **three** uses of the sugar produced by photosynthesis. (2)
3 Explain what is meant by a limiting factor. (2)
4 Explain why an increase in temperature can lead to an increase in the rate of photosynthesis. (2)
5 Describe the need for the control leaf 4 in Figure 1.21. (2)
6 Give an account of the carbon fixation stage of photosynthesis in a green leaf cell. (3)

Key Area 1.8
Respiration

Key points !

1 The chemical energy stored in **glucose** is released by most cells through a series of enzyme-controlled reactions called **respiration.** ☐
2 The energy released from the respiration of glucose is used to regenerate ATP from **ADP** and **phosphate.** ☐
3 The chemical energy stored in ATP can be released by breaking it down to ADP and phosphate. ☐
4 Energy can be used for cellular activities including muscle cell contraction, cell division, protein synthesis and transmission of nerve impulses. ☐
5 In respiration, glucose is broken down to produce **pyruvate** in the cytoplasm of cells. ☐
6 When oxygen is not available, pyruvate enters reaction pathways known as **fermentation.** ☐
7 If no oxygen is available, pyruvate is converted to **lactic acid** in animal cells and to **ethanol** and carbon dioxide in plant cells and in **yeast** cells. ☐
8 Breakdown of each glucose molecule via the fermentation pathway yields two molecules of ATP. ☐
9 Fermentation occurs in the cytoplasm. ☐
10 If oxygen is available, aerobic respiration occurs and pyruvate is further broken down into carbon dioxide and water within the mitochondria of cells. ☐
11 The breakdown of each glucose molecule via pyruvate to carbon dioxide and water in the presence of oxygen yields 38 molecules of ATP. ☐

Summary notes
What is respiration?

The chemical energy stored in sugar (glucose) is released by all cells through a series of enzyme-controlled reactions called respiration. The presence of energy in a foodstuff can be shown using the procedure in Figure 1.24. The energy is released by burning and the heat generated is used to raise the temperature of water.

The energy released from the breakdown of glucose is used to generate ATP by combining adenosine diphosphate (ADP) with additional phosphate. When the ATP is later broken down, its energy can be released and used in cellular activities such as muscle

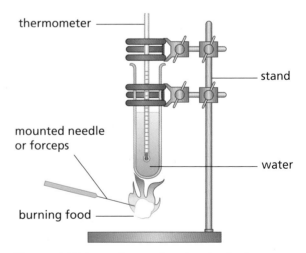

Figure 1.24 Release of energy from burning food

contraction, cell division, protein synthesis and the transmission of nerve impulses. The role of ATP in the transfer of energy for muscle contraction is shown in the wheel diagram in Figure 1.25.

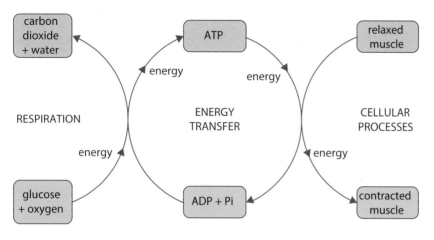

Figure 1.25 ATP wheel diagram

Cells that release a lot of energy in carrying out their functions have relatively large numbers of mitochondria, which are the sites of aerobic respiration. A sperm cell, which has a high energy requirement because of its need to move rapidly, has many mitochondria in its middle region (Figure 1.26). There is more about sperm cells in Key Area 2.4.

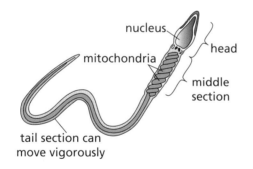

Figure 1.26 Mitochondria in a sperm cell

Breakdown of glucose by fermentation

Fermentation occurs in the cytoplasm and does not require the presence of oxygen. In fermentation, the first step involves the breakdown of each glucose molecule to pyruvate. In animal cells the pyruvate is then converted to lactic acid with the production of only 2 molecules of ATP per glucose molecule respired. In plant and yeast cells the pyruvate is converted to ethanol and carbon dioxide but, again, only 2 molecules of ATP are produced per glucose molecule respired. Fermentation in different cells is summarised in Figure 1.27.

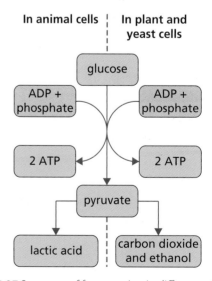

Figure 1.27 Summary of fermentation in different cells

Breakdown of glucose by aerobic respiration

In aerobic respiration, oxygen is used to complete the breakdown of glucose. Glucose molecules are broken down in two sets of steps. In the first the glucose is converted to pyruvate (pyruvic acid) in the cytoplasm and in the second the breakdown is completed in the mitochondria in the presence of oxygen to give carbon dioxide and water as the final products. For each molecule of glucose broken down, a total of 38 molecules of ATP are produced. This is summarised in Figure 1.28.

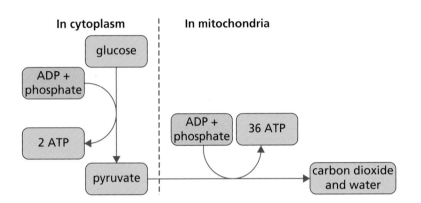

Figure 1.28 Summary of aerobic respiration

Key words

ADP and phosphate – substances that are combined to produce ATP
Ethanol – alcohol produced as a result of fermentation of sugars by yeast
Fermentation – a type of respiration without oxygen
Glucose – simple sugar used as a respiratory substrate for the production of ATP
Lactic acid – substance produced during fermentation in animals and responsible for muscle fatigue
Pyruvate – substance produced by the breakdown of glucose in the cytoplasm in fermentation or during the first stage of aerobic respiration
Respiration – a series of enzyme-controlled reactions resulting in the production of ATP from the chemical energy in glucose
Yeast – unicellular fungus used commercially in the brewing and baking industries

Questions ?

A Restricted-response questions (1 mark each)

1 Give the word equation for aerobic respiration.
2 State the purpose of aerobic respiration in cells.
3 Name the substance to which the energy released from the breakdown of glucose during aerobic respiration is transferred and describe how it is made.
4 Name the end products of aerobic respiration.
5 State the number of ATP molecules regenerated for each glucose molecule broken down in the process of aerobic respiration.

⇨

⇨
6 State the meaning of the term fermentation.
7 State the number of ATP molecules regenerated during the breakdown of one glucose molecule by fermentation.
8 State the location of fermentation in cells.
9 State the location of aerobic respiration in cells.
10 Give the role of mitochondria in aerobic respiration.

B Extended-response questions (2 or 3 marks)

1 Energy released during respiration is used for cellular activities. Give **three** examples of cellular activities that use this energy. (2)
2 Name the end products of fermentation in the following types of cell:
   a) yeast
   b) animal
   c) plant (2)
3 Compare aerobic respiration and fermentation in plant cells. (3)

Answers

Key Area 1.1

A Restricted-response questions (1 mark each)

1 nucleus, cytoplasm, cell membrane   [any 2]
2 nucleus, mitochondria, vacuole   [all 3]
3 plasmid
4 composed of different chemical substances, with different structures   [both]
5 site of release of energy/ATP production in aerobic respiration
6 do not contain chloroplasts
7 site of protein synthesis

B Extended-response questions (2 or 3 marks)

1 bacteria extremely small compared with plant cells; detail of structure of bacteria more difficult to observe with a microscope [1 each = 2]
2 made of tough material/cellulose; give cells support [1 each = 2]
3 a) large fluid-filled sac
   b) circular piece of DNA   [1 each = 2]
4 similarities – both have cell walls; genetic material; ribosomes. Differences – bacteria do not have mitochondria; chloroplasts; nuclei; bacterial cells are much smaller [2/1 similarities + 2/1 differences = 3]

Answers

Key Area 1.2

A Restricted-response questions (1 mark each)

1 lipid, protein   [both]
2 diffusion, osmosis   [both]
3 active processes require energy, passive ones do not
4 osmosis only involves water and occurs through membranes   [both]
5 a) turgid – plant cells stretched, full of water
   b) plasmolysed – plant cells shrunken through loss of water   [both]
6 plant roots taking up ions from their environment; nerve cells transporting potassium and sodium   [either]
7 the difference in concentration between two areas

B Extended-response questions (2 or 3 marks)

1 passive movement of molecules; from a region of high concentration to a region of lower concentration   [1 each = 2]
2 in osmosis allow passage of water molecules through pores; in active transport act as carriers   [1 each = 2]
3 potato would gain water by osmosis; because concentration of water outside greater than inside; cells would swell up; would become turgid and no more water would enter
   [any 3 = 3]
4 cell would lose water by osmosis; because water concentration in cells greater than outside water concentration; cells would shrink; cell functions would be damaged
   [any 3 = 3]

Answers

Key Area 1.3

A Restricted-response questions (1 mark each)

1 diploid
2 chromatids
3 move and guide chromatids to poles of the spindle
4 provides the dividing cells with growth substances and respiratory substrate

B Extended-response questions (2 or 3 marks)

1 DNA replicates; chromosomes appear as two chromatids   [1 each = 2]
2 b, d, a, c   [all correct = 2]

3 so that each daughter cell can receive an identical copy of the parent cell chromosomes; and so is able to carry out all cell functions   [1 each = 2]
4 so that the culture does not become contaminated by unwanted species; species that contaminate can be dangerous
   [1 each = 2]
5 cell culture relies on enzymes; enzyme activity affected by pH and temperature
   [1 each = 2]
6 maintains diploid chromosome number; leads to growth; allows repair after damage
   [1 each = 3]

Answers

Key Area 1.4

A Restricted-response questions (1 mark each)

1 carries genetic information
2 codes that allow proteins to be produced
3 double-stranded helix
4 A, G, T, C   [all]
5 A pairs with T, G pairs with C   [both]
6 gene
7 messenger RNA
8 ribosome

B Extended-response questions (2 or 3 marks)

1 each base matches its partner; their shapes fit into each other as a hand fits into a glove [1 each = 2]
2 mRNA has complementary copy of DNA base sequence; sequence of bases on mRNA determines sequence of amino acids in protein formed   [1 each = 2]
3 mRNA made in nucleus; carries complementary copy of DNA molecule; passes out of nucleus: moves to ribosome; amino acids assemble against the mRNA sequence of bases   [any 3 = 3]

Answers

Key Area 1.5

A Restricted-response questions (1 mark each)

1 sequence of amino acids
2 structural units; enzymes; hormones; receptors; antibodies   [any 4]
3 speed up chemical reactions in living organisms
4 molecular structure unchanged
5 otherwise reactions would be too slow to maintain life
6 substrate
7 active site
8 extremes of temperature or differences in pH [both]

B Extended-response questions (2 or 3 marks)

1 a) only works on one substrate
   b) best conditions for the reaction [1 each = 2]
2 active site shape becomes altered; can no longer fit its substrate   [1 each = 2]
3 speed up reactions in cells; unchanged by their activity; work best in optimum conditions; may be denatured by extremes of temperature or pH; specific to one substrate   [any 3 = 3]

Answers

Key Area 1.6

A Restricted-response questions (1 mark each)

1 in fertilisation; by plasmids; by viruses [any 1]
2 genetic engineering/genetic modification (GM)
3 supplied by source/donor; received by recipient/host [both]
4 vectors carry donor genes into recipients
5 cell that has been modified with DNA from another source
6 GM means a genetically modified organism with genes from another organism
7 insulin; growth hormone [either]

B Extended-response questions (2 or 3 marks)

1 d, b, c, a [all = 2, three in correct order = 1]
2 have plasmids that can be removed and have donor genes added; accept modified plasmids; reproduce very rapidly [any 2]
3 GM crops could interbreed with wild plants and contaminate their genetic information; genetic engineering might be applied to humans, leading to designer babies; there are religious/ethical issues [all 3 = 3]
4 insulin gene identified and extracted from human chromosome; plasmid removed from bacterium; human gene inserted into plasmid; modified plasmid inserted into bacterium; bacterium cultured and insulin extracted [any 3 = 3]

Answers

Key Area 1.7

A Restricted-response questions (1 mark each)

1 light-dependent stage; carbon fixation stage [both]
2 chlorophyll
3 ATP
4 oxygen diffuses into atmosphere; hydrogen passes to carbon fixation stage [both]
5 combines with hydrogen to form carbohydrate
6 temperature; light intensity; CO_2 concentration [all 3]

B Extended-response questions (2 or 3 marks)

1 water + carbon dioxide $\xrightarrow[\text{chlorophyll}]{\text{light}}$ sugar (glucose) + oxygen

[all = 2; 1 missing part = 1]

2 used in respiration; converted to starch; converted to cellulose; converted to lipid; converted to protein [any 3 = 2, 2/1 = 1]
3 factor close to its minimum value or in short supply; holds the rate of photosynthesis in check [1 each = 2]
4 raised temperature increases rate of enzyme action; enzymes needed for photosynthesis [1 each = 2]
5 used as control to compare with leaf 3; shows that enclosing in flask does not affect photosynthesis [1 each = 2]
6 CO_2 absorbed from atmosphere; combines with H from light stage; requires ATP from light stage; makes sugar; energy in ATP locked into sugar molecules [any 3 = 3]

Answers

Key Area 1.8

A Restricted-response questions (1 mark each)

1 glucose + oxygen → carbon dioxide + water + energy/38 ATP   [all]
2 to release energy from food
3 ATP is made from ADP and phosphate   [all]
4 CO_2, H_2O and ATP   [all]
5 38
6 a type of respiration without oxygen
7 2
8 cytoplasm
9 starts in cytoplasm and completes in the mitochondria   [both]
10 breakdown of pyruvate to CO_2 and H_2O and release of ATP   [all]

B Extended-response questions (2 or 3 marks)

1 muscle contraction; mitosis; protein synthesis; nerve transmission   [any 3 = 2, 2/1 = 1]
2 a) 2 ATP + ethanol + CO_2
  b) 2 ATP + lactic acid
  c) 2 ATP + ethanol + CO_2 [3 = 2, 2/1 = 1]
3 aerobic uses O_2, fermentation does not; aerobic produces 38 ATP, fermentation produces 2 ATP; aerobic produces CO_2 and H_2O, fermentation produces CO_2 and ethanol; aerobic occurs in mitochondria, fermentation occurs in the cytoplasm   [any 3 = 3]

Practice assessment: Unit 1 (40 marks)

Section A (10 marks)

1 Which line in the table below correctly shows the structures present in a bacterial cell?

	Cell wall	Nucleus	Ribosome
A	✓	✓	
B	✓		✓
C		✓	✓
D	✓	✓	

2 The following statements refer to transport across membranes:
  1 against the concentration gradient
  2 down the concentration gradient
  3 requires ATP
  4 is passive
  Which statements apply to diffusion?
  A 1 and 2
  B 1 and 3
  C 2 and 3
  D 2 and 4

3 Which molecule carries a copy of the genetic code from the nucleus to where protein is assembled?
  A DNA
  B ADP
  C mRNA
  D enzyme

4 Which term refers to the conditions under which an enzyme molecule works best?
  A specific
  B optimum
  C denatured
  D complementary

5 The following terms are related to genetic engineering:
  1 plasmid   2 vector   3 source chromosome
  Which of the above can carry donor genes into host cells?
  A 1 only
  B 1 and 2
  C 2 only
  D 2 and 3

⇨

6 Which **two** substances produced by the light-dependent stage of photosynthesis are needed for the carbon fixation stage?

A ATP and hydrogen

B chlorophyll and oxygen

C ATP and chlorophyll

D oxygen and hydrogen

7 Which line in the table below correctly shows information about fermentation in plant cells?

	Location	Products
A	cytoplasm	2 ATP + CO_2 and ethanol
B	mitochondria	2 ATP + CO_2 and ethanol
C	mitochondria	2 ATP + lactic acid
D	cytoplasm	2 ATP + lactic acid

8 The table below shows the number of cells present in a $0.1\,cm^3$ sample of a bacterial culture over a period of 5 hours.

Hour	Number of cells present ($\times$ 100)
0	0
1	14
2	24
3	48
4	100
5	200

What is the average hourly increase in the number of cells present **per cm^3** of culture solution?

A 40

B 400

C 4000

D 40 000

9 The apparatus below was set up to investigate the effect of temperature on the respiration rate of earthworms over 10-minute periods.

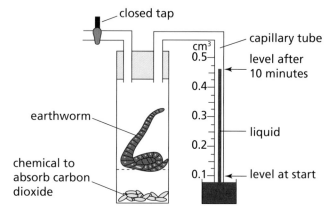

The experiment was repeated at three different temperatures and the rate of oxygen consumption by the worm calculated for each different temperature.

Which variable would have to be held constant for each repeat of the experiment?

A volume of oxygen consumed by the worm

B mass of worm used

C volume of coloured liquid in the capillary tube

D height of the wire platform in the glass tube

10 The diagram below shows the initial diameter of a disc of potato.

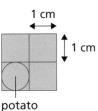

potato
disc

The disc was placed in pure water for 1 hour.
Which of the diagrams shows the expected diameter of the disc after this time?

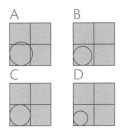

Section B (30 marks)

1 The diagram below shows a cell from human tissue. The cell has been magnified 500 times and the actual size of the magnified image is shown in the diagram. (1 mm = 1000 micrometres)

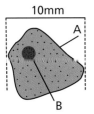

a) (i) Name structure A. (1)
(ii) Describe **one** way in which a fungal cell would differ from this cell. (1)
b) The cytoplasm of this cell contains few mitochondria.
Explain what this suggests about the function of the cell. (1)
c) Calculate the actual size of the cell in micrometres. (1SSI)

2 The diagram below shows a single plant cell immersed in a 10% sucrose solution. The concentration of the cell sap is equal to a 5% sucrose solution.

10% sucrose solution

5% sucrose
solution

a) Rewrite the sentence below, choosing the correct option from each set of brackets.
Water would move (into/out of) this cell by osmosis and the cell would become
(turgid/plasmolysed). (1)

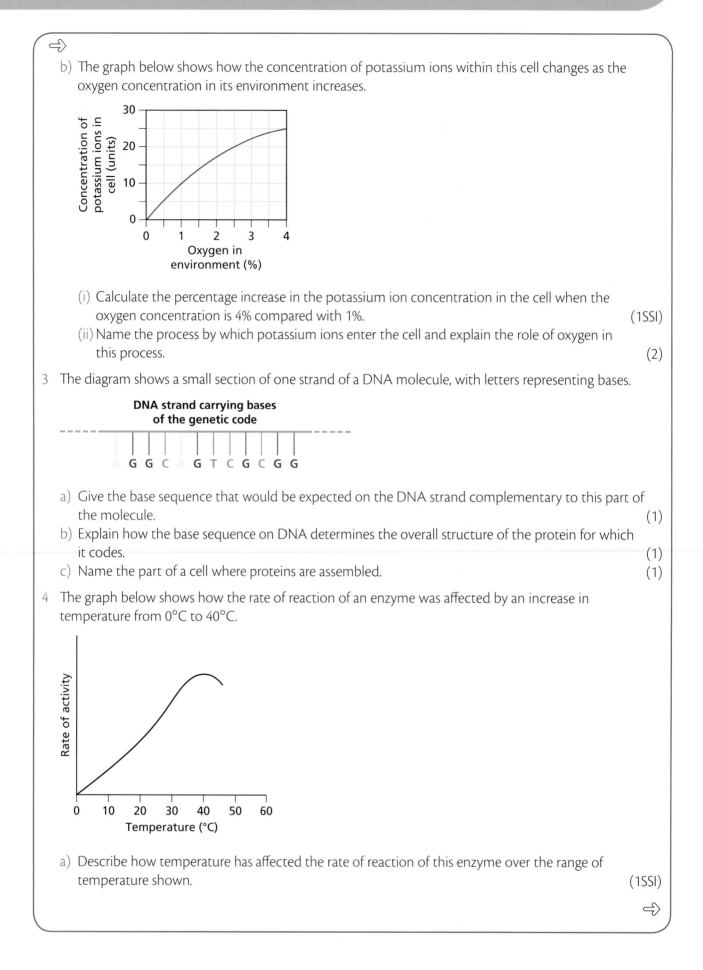

b) The graph below shows how the concentration of potassium ions within this cell changes as the oxygen concentration in its environment increases.

(i) Calculate the percentage increase in the potassium ion concentration in the cell when the oxygen concentration is 4% compared with 1%. (1SSI)

(ii) Name the process by which potassium ions enter the cell and explain the role of oxygen in this process. (2)

3 The diagram shows a small section of one strand of a DNA molecule, with letters representing bases.

**DNA strand carrying bases
of the genetic code**

A G G C A G T C G C G G

a) Give the base sequence that would be expected on the DNA strand complementary to this part of the molecule. (1)

b) Explain how the base sequence on DNA determines the overall structure of the protein for which it codes. (1)

c) Name the part of a cell where proteins are assembled. (1)

4 The graph below shows how the rate of reaction of an enzyme was affected by an increase in temperature from 0°C to 40°C.

a) Describe how temperature has affected the rate of reaction of this enzyme over the range of temperature shown. (1SSI)

⇨

b) Predict how the rate of reaction would change as the temperature was raised to 60°C, and give an explanation for your answer.

Prediction (1SSI)

Explanation (1)

c) Enzymes are proteins. Give **two** other functions of proteins. (1)

5 Genetic information can be transferred from one cell to another naturally or by genetic engineering.

a) Describe **one** way by which genetic information can be transferred naturally. (1)

b) The diagram below shows stages by which a gene from a human can be transferred artificially by genetic engineering to a bacterium.

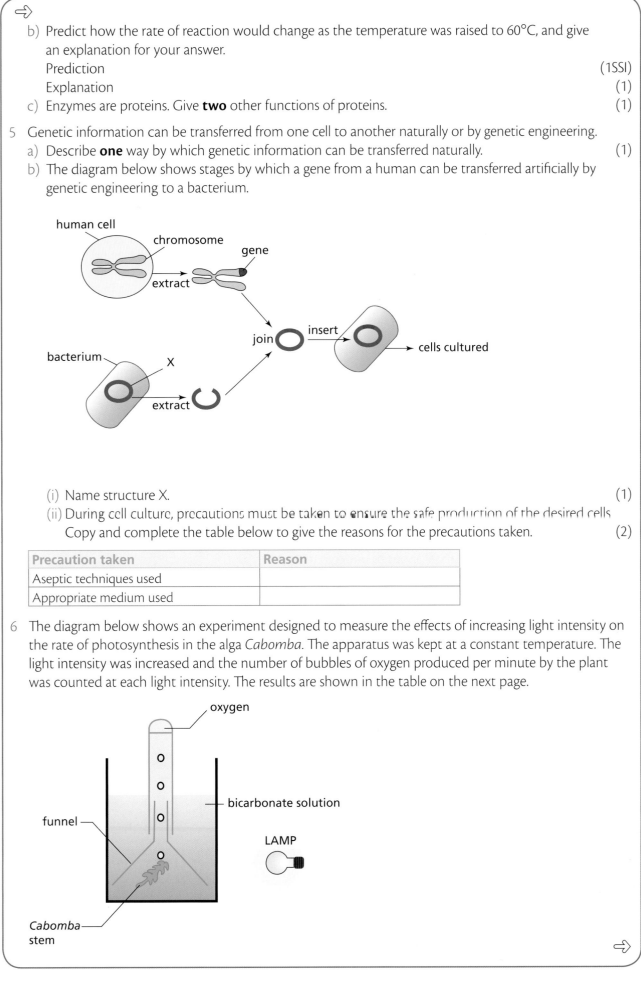

(i) Name structure X. (1)

(ii) During cell culture, precautions must be taken to ensure the safe production of the desired cells. Copy and complete the table below to give the reasons for the precautions taken. (2)

Precaution taken	Reason
Aseptic techniques used	
Appropriate medium used	

6 The diagram below shows an experiment designed to measure the effects of increasing light intensity on the rate of photosynthesis in the alga *Cabomba*. The apparatus was kept at a constant temperature. The light intensity was increased and the number of bubbles of oxygen produced per minute by the plant was counted at each light intensity. The results are shown in the table on the next page.

⇨

⇨

Light intensity (units)	Rate of photosynthesis (number of bubbles produced per minute)
10	18
20	34
30	70
40	130

a) On a piece of graph paper, draw a line graph to show the effect of light intensity on the rate of photosynthesis. (2SSI)

b) Apart from temperature, give **one** other variable that would have to be kept constant at each temperature to ensure that valid conclusions could be drawn. (1SSI)

7 The graph below shows the effect of light intensity on the rate of photosynthesis in a variety of tomato plants grown in controlled greenhouse conditions.

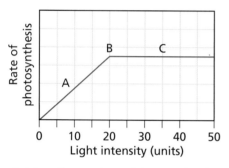

a) Identify a region of the graph where light intensity is the single limiting factor. (1SSI)

b) Suggest a factor, other than light intensity, that can limit the rate of photosynthesis in tomato plants. (1)

c) From the information given, suggest the light intensity at which the tomatoes should be grown to obtain the best yield with least energy input and justify your answer. (1SSI)

8 Describe the production of ATP as a molecule of glucose undergoes fermentation in a cell. (2)

9 The diagram shows an animal cell about to undergo mitosis.

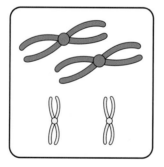

Describe the sequence of events of mitosis that would lead to this cell producing two daughter cells. (3)

Answers to practice assessment: Unit 1

Section A

1 B, 2 D, 3 C, 4 B, 5 B, 6 A, 7 A, 8 D, 9 B, 10 A

Section B

1 a) (i) cell membrane
   (ii) fungal cell would have a cell wall or vacuole
   b) cell uses little energy
   c) 20 micrometres
2 a) water would move out of the cell and it would become plasmolysed
   b) (i) 150%
      (ii) active transport
         oxygen allows aerobic respiration and release of energy
3 a) TCCGTCAGCGCC
   b) DNA base sequence determines the amino acids to be used and the order in which they occur
   c) ribosome
4 a) increasing temperature increases the rate of reaction up to 40°C but further increases decrease the rate
   b) prediction – reduced rate or reaction stops
      explanation – enzyme molecules denatured
   c) structural; antibodies; hormones; receptors   [any 2]
5 a) during fertilisation of gametes/transfer of plasmids between bacterial species/by viruses

b) (i) plasmid
   (ii)

Precaution taken	Reason
Aseptic techniques used	Prevent contamination of culture with other species of microorganism
Appropriate medium used	Ensure that correct nutrients and conditions for growth are present

6 a) scales and labels; plotting and joining   [both]

   b) concentration of CO_2 available from solution; mass/species of plant used   [either]

7 a) A
   b) temperature/CO_2 concentration
   c) 20 light intensity units; rate of photosynthesis does not increase even when light intensity is increased above this level
8 glucose acted upon by enzymes; converted to pyruvate; energy used to produce ATP from ADP and phosphate   [any 2]
9 spindle forms; chromosomes line up on equator; chromatids migrate to poles; new nuclei form   [any 3 = 3]

Multicellular Organisms

Cells, tissues and organs

Key points !

1 The cell is the basic unit of life. ☐
2 In multicellular organisms, different cells become **specialised** for different functions. ☐
3 Multicellular plants and animals have a variety of specialised cells. ☐
4 Specialised cells in the bodies of multicellular plants and animals are organised into groups called **tissues** and **organs**. ☐
5 A tissue is a group of similarly specialised cells carrying out the same broad function. ☐
6 An organ is made up of a group of different tissues working together. ☐
7 Different organs carry out different functions. ☐
8 Organs are organised into groups called organ **systems**. ☐

Summary notes

Cells

The cell is the basic unit of life. Look at page 2 (Figure 1.1) for a reminder of what individual cells look like.

In multicellular organisms, different cells become specialised to carry out different functions. Most cells within an organism have identical genetic material but in a particular type of specialised cell only some of it is used. Cells become specialised as their genetic material allows the production of specific proteins. These are different in different types of cell.

Multicellular plants and animals have a variety of specialised cells (Figure 2.1).

Specialisation of cells, in animals and plants, leads to the formation of a variety of tissues and organs.

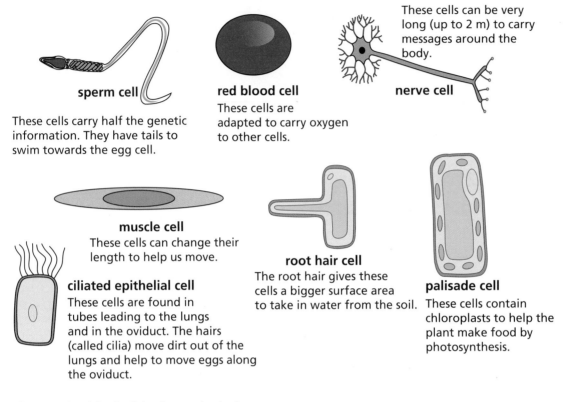

Figure 2.1 Specialised cells in plants and animals

Tissues

A living tissue is made from a group of cells with a similar structure and function, which all work together to do a particular job. Examples of animal tissues include muscle and nervous tissue. Plant tissues include xylem, phloem and root epidermis.

Organs

An organ is made up of a group of different tissues working together to perform a particular function. Different organs carry out different functions. Examples of organs in animals include the brain, heart, lungs, stomach and skin. Plant organs include the stem, root, leaf and flower (Figure 2.2).

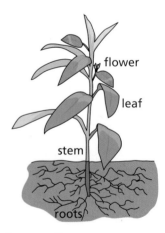

Figure 2.2 Plant organs

Organ systems

An organ system is made up of a group of different organs that work together to do a particular job. Examples of organ systems in animals include the skeletal system, muscular system, digestive system, respiratory system, nervous system and circulatory system. Plant systems include the vascular system in the shoots and the roots. Figure 2.3 outlines the structure and function of human and flowering plant organ systems.

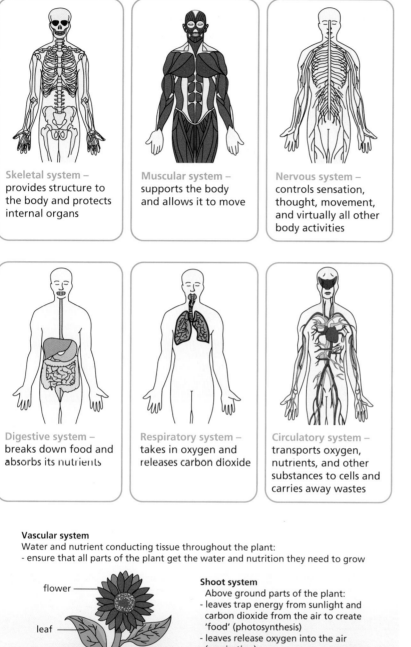

Skeletal system –
provides structure to
the body and protects
internal organs

Muscular system –
supports the body
and allows it to move

Nervous system –
controls sensation,
thought, movement,
and virtually all other
body activities

Digestive system –
breaks down food and
absorbs its nutrients

Respiratory system –
takes in oxygen and
releases carbon dioxide

Circulatory system –
transports oxygen,
nutrients, and other
substances to cells and
carries away wastes

(a)

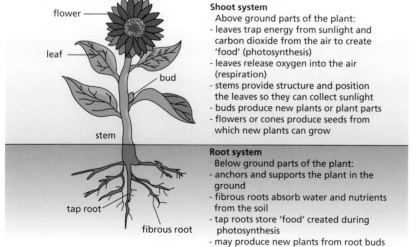

Vascular system
Water and nutrient conducting tissue throughout the plant:
- ensure that all parts of the plant get the water and nutrition they need to grow

flower

leaf

bud

stem

tap root

fibrous root

Shoot system
 Above ground parts of the plant:
- leaves trap energy from sunlight and
  carbon dioxide from the air to create
  'food' (photosynthesis)
- leaves release oxygen into the air
  (respiration)
- stems provide structure and position
  the leaves so they can collect sunlight
- buds produce new plants or plant parts
- flowers or cones produce seeds from
  which new plants can grow

Root system
 Below ground parts of the plant:
- anchors and supports the plant in the
  ground
- fibrous roots absorb water and nutrients
  from the soil
- tap roots store 'food' created during
  photosynthesis
- may produce new plants from root buds

(b)

Figure 2.3 Some organ systems in **(a)** humans and **(b)** flowering plants

Level of organisation

Cells, tissues, organs and systems are often referred to as the levels of
organisation within the body of an animal or plant. These levels of
organisation in the human circulatory system and the vascular system of
a flowering plant are summarised in Figure 2.4.

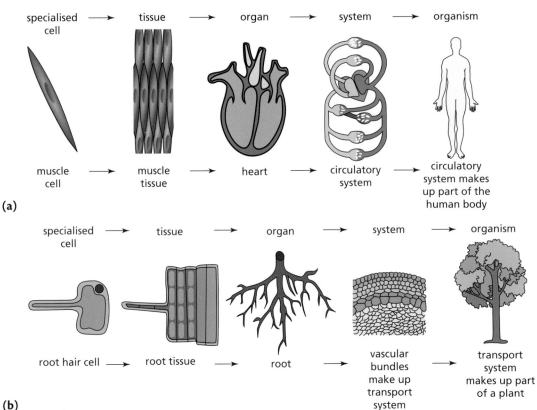

Figure 2.4 Levels of organisation in (a) the human circulatory system and (b) the vascular system in a flowering plant

Key words

Organ – a group of different tissues that work together to carry out a particular function, e.g. heart and lungs
Specialised – description of a cell that has become differentiated to carry out a particular function
System – a group of organs that work together to carry out a particular function, e.g. circulatory, respiratory and digestive
Tissue – a group of similar cells carrying out the same function

Questions ?

A Restricted-response questions (1 mark each)

1 Give the term applied to a group of similar cells that carry out the same function.
2 Give **one** example of a tissue from each of the following organisms:
  a) plant   b) human
3 State the meaning of the term organ.
4 Give **one** example of an organ from the following organisms.
  a) plant   b) human
5 Give the meaning of the term system.
6 Name **three** different human body systems.
7 Using information from Key Area 2.3, give the main functions of the human nervous system.
8 Using information from Key Area 2.4, give the main functions of the human reproductive system.
9 Using information from Key Area 2.6b, give the main functions of the human circulatory system.

B Extended-response questions (2 or 3 marks)

1 Explain what is meant by the term specialisation as applied to the development of cells. (2)
2 Describe the organisation in the human body with reference to tissues, organs and systems. (3)

Stem cells and meristems

Key points ❗

1 **Stem cells** are cells that can divide to form cells that can become specialised for different functions in multicellular animals. ☐
2 Stem cells are involved in the growth and development of animals. ☐
3 Stem cells are involved in the repair of damaged or diseased tissues in animals. ☐
4 **Meristems** are the sites of production of non-specialised cells in plants. ☐
5 Cells produced by meristems have the potential to become specialised and form a wide range of plant cells. ☐

Summary notes

Production of specialised cells in humans

The human body has many different types of specialised cell, which include skin cells, bone cells, muscle cells, nerve cells and blood cells. Specialised cells originate from stem cells, which are cells that have not yet specialised. Stem cells divide and produce cells that have the potential to become more specific cell types.

Types of stem cell

Different types of stem cell have different levels of potential (Figure 2.5). **Embryonic stem cells** are found in embryos and have the potential to divide and become nearly any type of cell in the body. **Adult stem cells** are found in tissues and organs in the body. Their differentiation is mainly restricted to forming the cell types of the tissue or organ in which they are found. In the growing body, adult stem cells are responsible for generating new tissue but once growth is complete, they are involved in the repair of damaged tissue. There are ethical issues surrounding the use of embryonic stem cells.

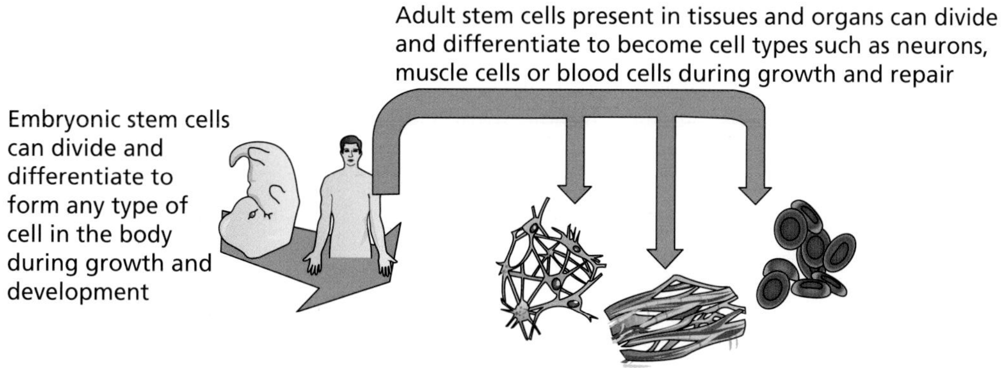

Embryonic stem cells can divide and differentiate to form any type of cell in the body during growth and development

Adult stem cells present in tissues and organs can divide and differentiate to become cell types such as neurons, muscle cells or blood cells during growth and repair

Figure 2.5 Embryonic and adult stem cells and their potential

Production of non-specialised cells in plant meristems

Meristems are sites of mitosis in most plants. They are regions of actively dividing cells, which have the potential to become almost any type of plant cell and contribute to plant growth.

Apical meristems are found at the shoot tip and at the root tip of plants while lateral meristems are found within the stems and roots (Figure 2.6). The shoot apical meristems give rise to organs such as leaves and flowers.

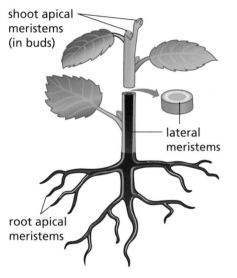

shoot apical
meristems
(in buds)

lateral
meristems

root apical
meristems

Figure 2.6 Meristems in plants

Ethical issues with embryonic stem cells

Embryonic stem cell research gives us a moral dilemma. It forces us to choose between two moral principles important to humans. The first is the duty to prevent or ease suffering by doing all we can to improve medical treatments for illness. The second is our duty to respect the value of human life.

In the case of embryonic stem cell research, it is very difficult to respect both of these moral principles.

Embryonic stem cell research could lead to new medical treatments, which could save human lives and relieve human suffering. On the other hand, to obtain embryonic stem cells, an early stage embryo has to be destroyed meaning the loss of a potential human life.

Which moral principle should be followed in this situation? Does the answer lie in our attitude to the embryo – does it have the status of a person?

What do you think about this issue?

Key words

Meristem – localised region of actively dividing cells in plants
Stem cell – unspecialised cell capable of dividing into cells that can develop into different cell types

Questions ?

A Restricted-response questions (1 mark each)

1 State what is meant by the term specialised, as applied to cells.
2 Give the general function of all stem cells.
3 Name a type of cell that can be formed when an adult human stem cell specialises.
4 Name the regions of plants where mitosis occurs.
5 Give the location of a region of mitosis in a plant.
6 Name **two** plant tissues that can be formed when plant cells specialise.

B Extended-response questions (2 or 3 marks)

1 Describe what happens to a stem cell that results in the production of a red blood cell in humans. (2)
2 Describe the similarities and differences between embryonic and adult stem cells. (3)
3 Describe the ethical issues surrounding research into human embryonic stem cells. (3)

Key Area 2.3a
Control and communication: nervous system

Key points !

1 The parts of the nervous system are the **brain**, **spinal cord**, the **nerves** and the **sense organs**. ☐
2 The nervous system is made up of cells called **neurons**. ☐
3 There are three basic types of neuron: **sensory**, **relay** and **motor**. ☐
4 The **central nervous system (CNS)** is made up of the brain and spinal cord. ☐
5 The brain is made up of the **cerebrum**, **cerebellum** and **medulla**. ☐
6 The cerebrum is responsible for conscious thoughts, reasoning, memory and emotions. ☐
7 The cerebellum controls balance and coordination. ☐
8 The medulla controls involuntary functions such as breathing, heart rate and peristalsis. ☐
9 The CNS processes information from sense organs and coordinates responses. ☐
10 Sense organs contain **receptor cells**, which generate electrical impulses in response to **stimuli**. ☐
11 Electrical impulses pass from sensory neurons to relay neurons within the CNS. ☐
12 Relay neurons within the CNS pass electrical impulses to motor neurons. ☐
13 Motor neurons pass electrical impulses to effectors, which bring about a response. ☐
14 Reflex actions are very rapid since they involve only a few neurons and do not require complex processing of information by the brain. ☐
15 Reflex actions help to protect the body from harm. ☐
16 The group of neurons involved with the structure and function of a reflex action is called a **reflex arc**. ☐
17 A **synapse** is a narrow gap between the neurons. ☐
18 Chemicals are released into the synapse from the neuron leading to it. These chemicals allow an electrical impulse to be generated in the next neuron after the synapse. ☐

Summary notes

Control and communication

Internal communication and control is required for the survival of a multicellular organism. This is because cells in the whole organism cannot function independently of each other. In animals there are two broad types of control, nervous and hormonal (see Key Area 2.3b on page 60).

Nervous control in animals

The nervous system of mammals has two main parts: the central nervous system (CNS), which consists of the brain and spinal cord, and the nerves (neurons), which connect the CNS to all parts of the body (Figure 2.7).

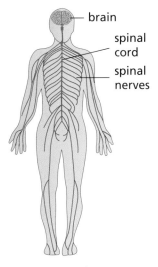

brain

spinal cord

spinal nerves

Figure 2.7 Parts of the human nervous system

The nervous system receives stimuli, which are pieces of information about the external and internal environment of the body. Stimuli are received by receptors. The sensory information received is passed into the central nervous system (CNS) where it is processed. The CNS sorts out stimuli received from sense organs and sends electrical impulses along nerves to effectors. The effectors are the muscles or glands that make the appropriate response (Figure 2.8).

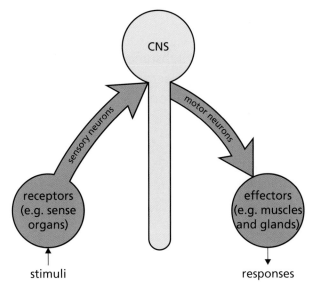

Figure 2.8 Flow of information in the nervous system

Cells of the nervous system

The nervous system is made up from fibre-shaped cells called neurons. Nerves are bundles of neurons. Neurons are the longest cells of the body. There are three main types (Figure 2.9).

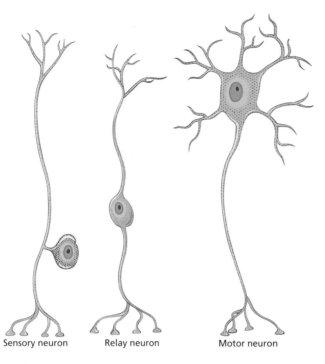

Figure 2.9 Types of neuron

Sensory neurons carry messages from the receptors in the sense organs towards the CNS. In the CNS there are shorter interconnecting relay neurons that connect sensory neurons to motor neurons. Motor neurons carry messages from the CNS to the muscles or glands that are the effectors. Motor neurons enable the effectors to make a response, which can be a rapid action from a muscle or a slower response from a gland.

Synapses

A synapse is a gap between neurons. Chemical transmitter substances released from tiny vacuoles at the end of one neuron diffuse across the synapse to generate an electrical impulse in the next neuron (Figure 2.10).

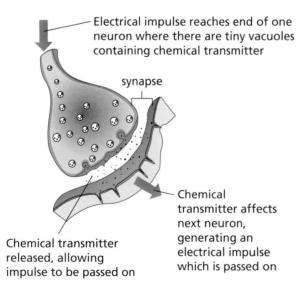

Figure 2.10 A synapse

Rapid reflex action

Reflexes are rapid, automatic and protective actions (see the table below). They are automatic responses to damaging stimuli. We do not have to learn or think about the response because that could cause delay and lead to further damage to the body.

Reflex action	Protective value
Cough	Clears the windpipe
Sneeze	Clears nasal passages
Blink	Clears the eye surfaces
Withdrawal	Removes body from extreme heat and pain

The reflex arc

The table below shows the pathway of a withdrawal reflex action from the detection of a heat stimulus to the withdrawal response.

Stage in withdrawal reflex	Description of stage
Stimulus	The touch of a hot object
Sense organ	Heat receptor cells in skin detect the stimulus
Sensory neuron	Messages carried as electrical impulses to the CNS
Relay neuron	Messages passed as electrical impulses through the CNS to motor neurons
Motor neuron	Messages carried as electrical impulses to the muscle
Muscle	Muscle contracts
Response	Withdrawal from the extreme heat

Figure 2.11 shows the reflex arc as a diagram.

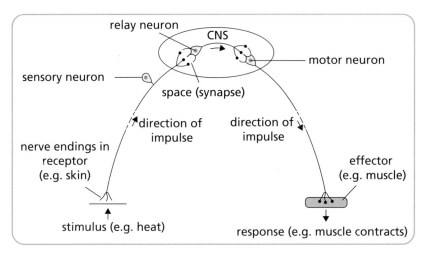

Figure 2.11 Reflex arc

The brain

The human brain is an extremely complex organ, made up of hundreds of billions of neurons. It can be divided into three different regions (Figure 2.12).

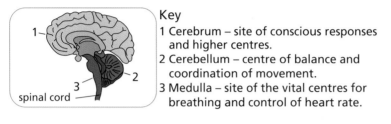

Key
1 Cerebrum – site of conscious responses and higher centres.
2 Cerebellum – centre of balance and coordination of movement.
3 Medulla – site of the vital centres for breathing and control of heart rate.

Figure 2.12 Side view of the brain sliced down the middle

Each region has specific functions associated with it, as outlined in the following table.

Region	Function
Cerebrum	Site of conscious thoughts, reasoning, memory and emotions
Cerebellum	Centre of control for balance and coordination of movement
Medulla	Centre of control for breathing, heart rate and peristalsis

Key words

Brain – organ of the central nervous system of mammals where vital functions are coordinated
Central nervous system (CNS) – part of the nervous system made up of the brain and spinal cord
Cerebellum – part of the brain that controls balance and coordination of movement
Cerebrum – large folded part of the brain that controls conscious responses, memory, thought, intelligence and emotions
Medulla – part of the brain controlling breathing, heart rate and peristalsis
Motor neuron – nerve cell that carries electrical impulses from the CNS to effectors such as muscles or glands
Nerves – specialised tissues that connect receptors to the CNS and the CNS to the effectors
Neuron – nerve cell that is specialised to transmit electrical impulses
Sense organs – organs with receptor cells adapted to detect specific stimuli
Sensory neuron – nerve cell that transmits electrical impulses from a sense organ to the CNS
Receptor cell – cell that can detect stimuli inside or outside the body
Reflex arc – pathway of information from a sensory neuron through a relay neuron directly to a motor neuron
Relay neuron – nerve cell that transmits electrical impulses from sensory neurons to motor neurons
Spinal cord – part of the central nervous system of a mammal that runs within its backbone
Stimuli – changes in the environment detected by receptor cells that trigger a response in an organism (*sing.* stimulus)
Synapse – gap between two neurons

Questions ?

A Restricted-response questions (1 mark each)

1 Name the two parts of the human central nervous system (CNS).
2 State how information is passed along neurons.
3 State how neurons are linked in the nervous system.
4 State the general function of receptors as part of the nervous system.
5 Give the importance of the rapid reflex action in humans.

B Extended-response questions (2 or 3 marks)

1 Describe the role of the CNS in humans. (2)
2 Describe the functions of each of the following parts of the brain.
  a) cerebrum
  b) cerebellum
  c) medulla (2)
3 Describe the role of each of the following cell types in the nervous system.
  a) sensory neurons
  b) relay neurons
  c) motor neurons (2)
4 Describe what happens when an electrical signal arrives at a synapse. (3)
5 Describe the flow of information along a reflex arc. (3)

Key Area 2.3b
Control and communication: endocrine system

Key points !

1 **Endocrine glands** release hormones into the bloodstream. ☐
2 Hormones are proteins that act as chemical messengers. ☐
3 Hormones affect **target organs**, which contain cells with receptors to detect them. ☐
4 Receptors are specific so that only target tissues are affected by specific hormones. ☐
5 The **pancreas** monitors the blood glucose concentration in the blood. ☐
6 The pancreas produces the hormones **insulin** and **glucagon**. ☐
7 Insulin is released in response to increased blood glucose concentration and stimulates the **liver** to convert excess glucose to **glycogen** for storage. ☐
8 Glucagon is released in response to decreased blood glucose concentration and stimulates the liver to release glucose from stored glycogen. ☐

Summary notes

Hormonal control in animals

Endocrine glands release hormones into the blood stream. Hormones are chemical messengers which are transported in the blood to their target organ. Target organs have cells with specific receptor molecules on their surfaces. Although hormones are carried to all the body organs they only affect their target organs, which respond to them.

Since hormones are transported in the blood, hormonal control is slower than nervous control. Examples of glands, hormones, target organs and effects are shown in the table below.

Gland	Hormone	Target organ	Effect
Pituitary gland	Anti-diuretic hormone (ADH)	Kidney	Control of blood water concentration
Thyroid gland	Thyroxine	Various	Control of metabolic rate
Pancreas	Insulin	Liver	Control of blood glucose concentration
Adrenal gland	Adrenaline	Various	Control of nervous system function

Blood glucose regulation in humans

Carbohydrate intake by eating increases the blood glucose concentration. A rise in blood glucose concentration is detected by receptor cells in the pancreas. This causes the pancreas to produce the hormone insulin.

Insulin travels in the blood to its target organ, the liver, and stimulates it to take up glucose and store it as glycogen. This reduces the blood glucose concentration.

Missing a meal or taking a lot of exercise can result in a decrease in the blood glucose concentration. A decrease in blood glucose concentration is detected by different receptor cells in the pancreas. This causes the pancreas to produce the hormone glucagon. Glucagon travels in the blood to its target organ, the liver, and causes the liver cells to convert glycogen to glucose. The glucose is released, increasing the blood glucose concentration. This is summarised in Figure 2.13.

Hints & tips

GLUcaGON is needed when GLUcose is GONe.

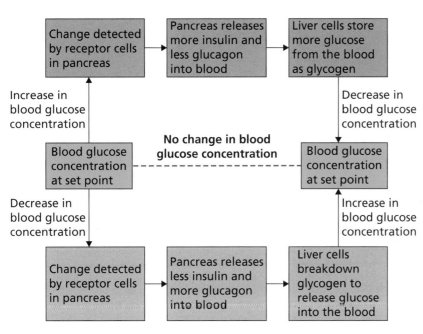

Figure 2.13 Summary of the control of the glucose concentration in the blood.

Hints & tips

A useful rhyme:
Low blood sugar – glucose gone; what you need is glucagon

To turn glucose into glycogen; what you need is insulin

Hints & tips

This is an occasion when spelling is very important. You must not confuse glycogen and glucagon.

In recent years there has been a huge increase in the number of people in Scotland with diabetes.

Diabetes

The issue of diabetes is raised in Key Area 2.7 where the role of lifestyle choices is discussed. In Key Area 1.6, the part played by genetic engineering in the production of the artificial insulin needed to treat diabetes is explained.

Diabetes is an example of a communication pathway that has failed. It is caused by failure to control glucose levels in the body. There are two forms of the disease:

● **Type 1 diabetes** is a severe insulin deficiency, which usually appears in childhood. Until the discovery of insulin in 1922, diabetes was a fatal disease. Today diabetes can be treated by injections with insulin or by careful diet and tablets. Insulin can be extracted from the pancreas tissue of cattle and pigs, or it

⇨

⇨

can be made in fermenters by genetically engineered bacteria. Treatment is improving all the time, with the development of fast-acting and slow-acting insulin preparations, simpler injection pens, oral insulin preparations, portable insulin infusion pumps and even the possibility of tissue transplants and stem cell therapy.

● **Type 2 diabetes** occurs because, although insulin is made, insulin receptors in the target tissues do not respond and so the hormone has no effect. The treatment of this form of diabetes involves regulation of blood glucose through strict control of diet. Type 2 diabetes tends to appear in overweight people and is increasing. It accounts for 90% of diabetes cases in Scotland and is linked to lifestyle choices involving a diet leading to obesity.

Key words

Endocrine gland – gland that produces and releases a hormone directly into the blood

Glucagon – hormone produced by the pancreas, responsible for triggering the conversion of glycogen into glucose in the liver

Glycogen – animal storage carbohydrate located in the liver and muscle tissues

Insulin – hormone produced by the pancreas that triggers the conversion of glucose into glycogen in the liver

Liver – large organ, beside the stomach, with many important functions including a role in blood glucose control

Pancreas – organ responsible for the production of digestive enzymes and the hormones insulin and glucagon

Target organ – organ with receptor molecules on its cell surfaces that recognise a specific hormone

Questions ?

A Restricted-response questions (1 mark each)

1 State the function of endocrine glands.
2 Give **two** examples of endocrine glands in humans.
3 State how hormones carry their messages around the body.
4 Give the term applied to cells containing receptors sensitive to a specific hormone.
5 Name **two** hormones involved in the control of blood glucose concentration.
6 Give a reason for the increase in individuals with type 2 diabetes.

B Extended-response questions (2 or 3 marks)

1 Explain how the action of hormones is specific. (2)
2 Describe the role of the pancreas in the regulation of blood glucose. (2)
3 Describe the role of the liver in the regulation of blood glucose. (2)
4 Describe the control of blood glucose concentration in humans. (3)
5 Describe the two types of diabetes. (3)

Key Area 2.4
Reproduction

Summary notes
Chromosomes, gametes and reproduction

The cells in the bodies of most multicellular organisms are diploid, which means that they contain two matching sets of chromosomes. Multicellular organisms produce sex cells called gametes, which are usually haploid. Haploid cells contain one set of chromosomes. Gametes are either male or female.

Reproduction in flowering plants

In flowering plants, gametes are produced in the flowers. Male gametes are inside the pollen grains produced in the anthers of flowers. Female gametes are inside the ovules produced in the ovaries. These structures are shown in Figure 2.14.

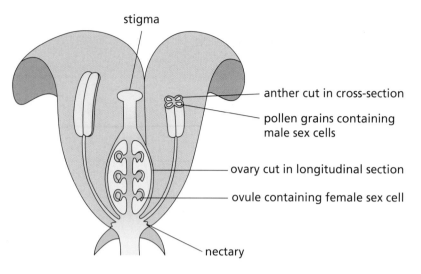

Figure 2.14 Flower structure

Most pollen grains are either light to blow in the wind or spiky to catch onto animal pollinators. During pollination, pollen grains are carried by wind or animals and land on the stigma of a flower of the correct species, where they germinate. A pollen tube grows into the ovary, where it reaches an ovule. The nucleus of the pollen grain then passes along the pollen tube and joins with a nucleus in the ovule. The fusion of haploid gametes produces a diploid zygote.

After fertilisation, the female parts of the flower develop into a fruit. The ovules become seeds and the ovary wall becomes the rest of the fruit.

Reproduction in animals

In animals, gametes are produced in specialised organs. Figure 2.15 shows the reproductive organs in human males and females. Male gametes are sperm cells and are produced in the testes. Female gametes are called ova and are produced in the ovaries. Sperm cells have tails that allow them to swim to ova. The ova have a food supply. After fertilisation, the food supply feeds the early embryo.

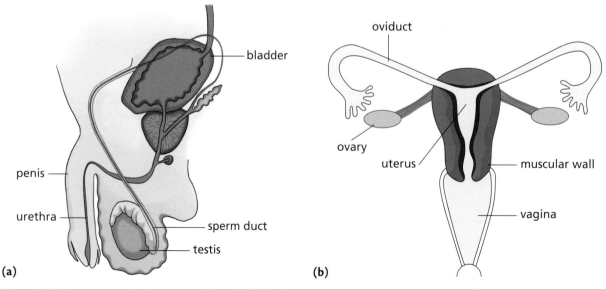

(a)   **(b)**

Figure 2.15 Human reproductive organs: **(a)** male, **(b)** female

In both plants and animals, the fusion of haploid gametes produces a diploid zygote. Figure 2.16 shows fertilisation in humans. There is more about chromosome number and cell division in Key Area 1.3.

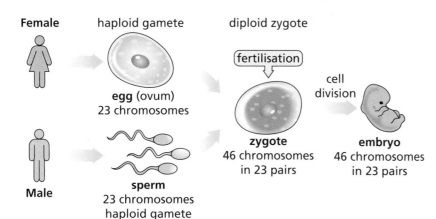

Figure 2.16 Fertilisation in humans

Key words

Anther – organ within a flower that produces pollen grains
Fertilisation – the fusion of gametes
Gamete – sex cell containing the haploid chromosome number
Motile – able to move under its own power
Ova – female gametes produced by ovaries in animals (*sing.* ovum)
Ovaries – female sex organs (*sing.* ovary)
Ovule – structure containing a female gamete, produced by ovaries in plants
Pollen grain – structure produced in the anthers of a flower that contains the male gamete
Pollination – transfer of a pollen grain from anther to stigma, usually by wind or an animal pollinator
Sperm cell – gamete produced in the testes of male animals
Testes – male sex organs in animals for the production of sperm
Zygote – fertilised egg cell

Questions ?

A Restricted-response questions (1 mark each)

1 Give the meaning of the following terms:
   a) haploid   b) diploid
2 Name the sites of gamete production in plants.
3 Name the male and female gametes in plants.
4 Name the sites of gamete production in animals.
5 Name the male and female gametes in animals.
6 Describe the process of fertilisation.
7 Explain why body cells are diploid and gametes are haploid.
8 Give the term used for a fertilised egg cell.
9 Using information in Key Area 1.3, name the process by which diploid cells are maintained as an organism grows.

B Extended-response questions (2 or 3 marks)

1 Describe the differences between a sperm cell and an ovum. (2)
2 Describe how fertilisation is achieved in a flowering plant. (3)

Variation and inheritance

Key points !

1 Differences that can be seen between individual members of a species are called **variation**. ☐
2 In **discrete** variation, the differences in a characteristic are clear-cut and show a **discontinuous** pattern. ☐
3 In **continuous** variation there is a range of variation between the extremes of a characteristic. ☐
4 Discrete variation arises because individuals carry different **alleles** of the discrete **genes** for the characteristic. ☐
5 In continuous variation, the characteristic is usually **polygenic**, which means that different alleles of many different genes are involved. ☐
6 The **phenotype** of an organism is the outward appearance of a characteristic it has. ☐
7 The **genotype** of an organism is a statement of the alleles it has for a characteristic. ☐
8 **Dominant** alleles always show in the phenotype of an organism that has them. ☐
9 **Recessive** alleles only show themselves in the phenotype if an organism has inherited one from each parent. ☐
10 A **homozygous** organism has two copies of the same allele of a particular gene; one from each parent. ☐
11 A **heterozygous** organism has inherited two different alleles of the same gene; one from each parent. ☐

Summary notes

Discrete and continuous variation

Differences that can be seen between individual members of a species are called variation.

In discrete variation, the differences are clear-cut and show a discontinuous pattern. A good example is the human ability to roll the tongue – an individual can either do it or is unable to – it is clear-cut. Discrete variation arises because individuals carry different discrete forms of the gene for the characteristic.

In continuous variation there is a range of variation between extremes. The characteristic is usually polygenic, which means that many different genes are involved. Most features of an individual's phenotype are polygenic and show continuous variation. A good example is human height, which shows a range from very short individuals to very tall individuals and there are all possible heights in between.

Figure 2.17 shows examples of the patterns of discrete and continuous variation.

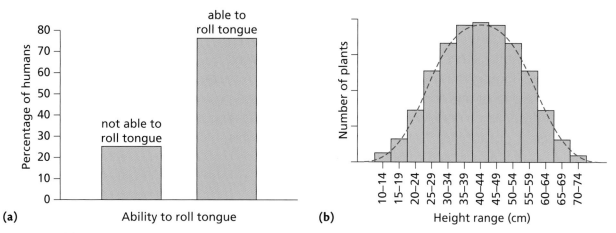

Figure 2.17 (a) Discrete variation – tongue-rolling bar chart **(b)** Continuous variation – height line graph/histogram

What is a gene?

A gene is a single piece of genetic information made from DNA. It carries the information to create a particular characteristic. Genes exist in different forms called alleles, which give different versions of the same characteristic. Alleles are given symbols, usually letters of the alphabet, to make working with them easier. The table below shows some examples of organisms and the alleles of one of their genes.

Organism	Gene	Allele symbol	What the allele does in the organism
Human	Tongue-rolling	R	Allows the tongue to be rolled up from the sides
		r	Tongue cannot be rolled up from the sides
Fruit fly	Wing length	W	Normal length of wings
		w	Very short wings – they cannot fly
Pea plant	Seed colour	Y	Pea seeds yellow coloured
		y	Pea seeds green coloured

Genetics and its language

Genetics is the study of variation and inheritance and it has its own language, which is best understood through an example. In the early nineteenth century an Austrian monk called Gregor Mendel studied inheritance in garden pea plants. He noted that the plants produced yellow or green peas and started experiments to study how pea seed colour was inherited. Mendel was able to show that each individual pea plant had two sets of genetic information, a set from each of its two parents. This meant that it had two alleles of each gene – these could be the same or different. A plant with two alleles the same is said to be homozygous while a plant with different alleles is heterozygous. The alleles the plant has form its genotype but the appearance of the seed is the phenotype. An individual plant passes on only one of its two alleles into gametes to be inherited by offspring.

Mendel also showed that alleles could be dominant or recessive – dominant alleles always showed up in the phenotype of a plant while recessive alleles only showed up if a plant had two copies. It turned out that yellow seed colour was dominant to green seed colour. We give dominant alleles a capital letter symbol and recessive alleles a lower case letter symbol. Homozygous plants always breed true, which means that their characteristics always appear in their offspring's phenotype. Heterozygous individuals do not always breed true and their offspring might have different phenotypes. The table below summarises this information in relation to pea seed colour.

Genotype	Phenotype	Homozygous or heterozygous	Description of breeding
YY	Yellow seeds	Homozygous dominant	True-breeding for yellow seeds
Yy	Yellow seeds	Heterozygous	Hybrid, which does not breed true
yy	Green seeds	Homozygous recessive	True-breeding for green seeds

Mendel carried out a classic experiment, which has helped us to understand the inheritance of a single pair of contrasting alleles in garden peas.

Summary of Mendel's experiment

Parents (Mendel selected these from greenhouse stock)

Phenotype: True breeding with   ×   True breeding with
yellow seeds   green seeds

Genotype: **YY** (homozygous)   **yy** (homozygous)

Gametes: All contain **Y**   All contain **y**

Fertilisation: **Y** gametes fertilise **y** gametes and so all offspring are **Yy**

Offspring (F$_1$)

Genotype: All **Yy** (heterozygous)

Phenotype: All hybrids with yellow seeds because **Y** is dominant to **y**

Parents (Mendel crossed the F$_1$ generation by pollinating individuals with their own pollen)

Phenotypes: Hybrid with yellow seeds   ×   Hybrid with yellow seeds

Genotypes: **Yy** (heterozygous)   **Yy** (heterozygous)

Gametes: Both **Y** and **y**   Both **Y** and **y**

Fertilisation (various fertilisations are possible in the proportions shown in the following table)

Gametes	Y	y
Y	YY	Yy
y	Yy	yy

Offspring (F$_2$)

Phenotypes: 75% yellow seeds (**YY** and **Yy**) and 25% green seeds (**yy**)

This can be expressed as a ratio of 3 plants with yellow seeds : 1 plant with green seeds.

An example of human inheritance: cystic fibrosis (CF) in a family

Cystic fibrosis (CF) is caused when an individual inherits two copies of a recessive allele **c**. In the imaginary **family tree** in Figure 2.18, individuals 2, 3 and 4 are heterozygous for this condition. Each has the genotype **Cc**, which means that they do not have the condition but could each pass the **c** allele on to offspring – they are carriers. Individual 2 has passed **c** to her daughter 3 whose partner, 4, is also a carrier. In situations like this one, individuals 3 and 4 might receive **genetic counselling** before starting a family. This could help inform them of the chances of their offspring inheriting the condition and the implications involved. Can you work out the chances of their children inheriting CF?

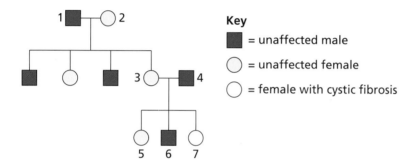

Key
■ = unaffected male
○ = unaffected female
○ = female with cystic fibrosis

Figure 2.18 Cystic fibrosis in a family tree

Key words

Allele – a form of a gene
Discontinuous – alternative term for discrete variation, which is variation that is clear-cut and observable
Discrete – variation that is clear-cut and observable as categories
Dominant – form of a gene that is expressed in the phenotype, whether homozygous or heterozygous
Family tree – diagram that shows the inheritance of a genetic condition in a family
Genetic counselling – medical procedure in which individuals can receive advice and information about an inherited condition
Genotype – the alleles that an organism has for a particular characteristic, usually written as symbols
Heterozygous – describes a genotype in which the two alleles for the characteristic are different
Homozygous – describes a genotype in which the two alleles for the characteristic are the same
Phenotype – the visible characteristics of an organism that occur as a result of its genes
Polygenic – inheritance determined by the interaction of several genes acting together
Recessive – allele of a gene that only shows in the phenotype if the genotype is homozygous for that allele
Variation – differences in characteristics that can be seen between individual members of a species

Questions ?

A Restricted-response questions (1 mark each)

1 Give the term used to describe the differences that exist between organisms of the same species.
2 State what is meant by the following terms:
   a) continuous variation
   b) discrete variation
3 Give an example of a characteristic in humans that shows continuous variation.
4 Give an example of a characteristic in humans that shows discrete variation.
5 State what is meant by the term polygenic.
6 In the human cystic fibrosis example on page 69, what is the chance that a child of two heterozygous parents would inherit the condition?

B Extended-response questions (2 or 3 marks)

1 Describe the difference between the terms gene and allele. (2)
2 Describe the difference between the terms genotype and phenotype. (2)
3 Describe the difference between the terms homozygous and heterozygous. (2)
4 Describe the difference between the terms dominant and recessive. (2)
5 Give the genotypes of individuals 4 and 7 in the family tree in Figure 2.18. (2)
6 Using information in Key Area 3.4, describe the importance of variation to a species. (3)

Key Area 2.6a
The need for transport in plants

Key points !

1 Plants require water for transporting materials such as **minerals**, for photosynthesis and for the maintenance of turgidity. ☐
2 Plants take up water by osmosis and minerals from the soil through the **root epidermis**. ☐
3 **Root hair cells** increase the surface area of the root epidermis. ☐
4 Water and minerals taken up by roots are passed into tubes made up of dead **xylem cells**. ☐
5 The cell walls of xylem cells contain a tough woody substance called **lignin**. ☐
6 Water and minerals pass through the plant stems to the leaves through xylem vessels. ☐
7 Water enters leaves in xylem vessels and passes into **spongy mesophyll** cells by osmosis. ☐
8 Water evaporates into spaces in the spongy mesophyll. ☐
9 Water vapour diffuses out of leaves through pores in the leaf epidermis called **stomata**. ☐
10 The stomata open and close by movements of **guard cells** found on either side of each pore. ☐
11 Loss of water through the leaves of a plant is called **transpiration**. ☐
12 Sugars made by photosynthesis are transported around plants in **phloem** tubes, which are made from living cells. ☐
13 Phloem and xylem make up the **vascular tissue** of flowering plants. ☐

Summary notes
The need for water

Plants require water because it is a raw material for photosynthesis (Key Area 1.7), providing the hydrogen to convert carbon dioxide gas to sugar. The sugar produced by photosynthesis and minerals absorbed from the soil are transported around the plant dissolved in water. Water is also required for the maintenance of turgor in cells giving the plant support (Key Area 1.2). It can also help cool plants when it evaporates from leaves – see the table below.

Use of water	Note
Photosynthesis	Hydrogen from water combines with carbon dioxide to produce sugar
Transport	Minerals and sugars are transported dissolved in water
Support	Water swells vacuoles making cells turgid
Cooling	Evaporation of water from leaves has a cooling effect

Plant transport systems

Water

Plants have a transport system for carrying water and minerals. Vast amounts of water pass through plants but only 1% of this is used by the plant cells for photosynthesis and turgor. The remaining 99% evaporates from the leaves and is lost to the atmosphere.

Movement of water into plants occurs by osmosis into the root hairs. Water and minerals are transported into xylem cells, then up through the plant roots and stem. Xylem cells are lignified to withstand the high pressure that builds up when water is moving through the plant. The lignified xylem also gives plant stems the strength to withstand wind.

Xylem carries water and minerals into leaves and into mesophyll tissue where some water is used in photosynthesis. Most water is lost by evaporation into air spaces in mesophyll and then out through pores called stomata in the leaf epidermis. Each stoma is formed between a pair of guard cells, whose action can open or close the pore. Loss of water by evaporation and transpiration lowers the concentration of water in mesophyll cells and so allows them to take up water from xylem tissues below. Movement of water in a plant is summarised in Figure 2.19.

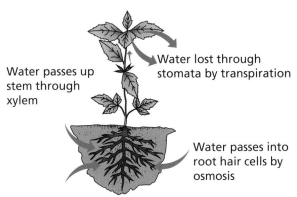

Water passes up stem through xylem

Water lost through stomata by transpiration

Water passes into root hair cells by osmosis

Figure 2.19 Water movement in a plant

Sugars

Sugars made in photosynthesis are transported around the plant in phloem. Phloem cells are alive and able to transport sugars from photosynthetic tissues to all parts of the plant where they are needed for respiration. Phloem tissue usually runs alongside xylem tissues in the vascular tissues within the organs of the plant (Figure 2.20).

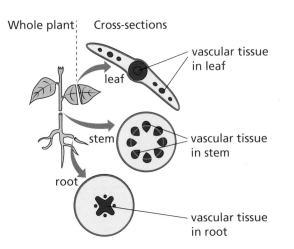

Whole plant | Cross-sections

vascular tissue in leaf

leaf

stem

vascular tissue in stem

root

vascular tissue in root

Figure 2.20 Distribution of vascular tissues in a plant

Key words

Guard cells – found on either side of a stoma; they control gas exchange in leaves by controlling opening and closing of the stoma

Lignin – carbohydrate material lining the xylem vessels and providing strength and support

Minerals – nutrient ions essential for healthy growth

Phloem – vessels in plants that transport sugars

Root epidermis – outer layer of cells of a root

Root hair cell – specialised cell that increases the surface area of the root epidermis to improve the uptake of water and minerals

Spongy mesophyll – plant leaf tissue with loosely packed cells and air spaces between them to allow gas exchange

Stomata – tiny pores in the leaf epidermis that allow gas exchange (*sing.* stoma)

Transpiration – evaporation of water through the stomata of leaves

Vascular tissue – plant tissue consisting of phloem and xylem that transports material in a plant

Xylem vessels – narrow, dead tubes with lignin in their walls for the transport of water and minerals in plants

Questions ?

A Restricted-response questions (1 mark each)

1 Give **two** reasons why plants need a transport system.
2 Give **two** examples of substances that need to be transported around a plant.
3 Give the structure of a xylem vessel.
4 State the part played by xylem vessels in plant transport.
5 Name the process by which water vapour evaporates through the stomata of leaves.
6 State the role of the guard cells in the epidermis of a leaf.
7 State the role of phloem tubes in the transport system of a plant.

B Extended-response questions (2 or 3 marks)

1 Give **three** reasons why plants require water.   (2)
2 Describe the uptake of water by plant roots and the role of the root hair cells in the root epidermis in this process.   (2)
3 Describe the role of the spongy mesophyll in pulling water through xylem vessels.   (2)
4 Describe the uptake and movement of water through a plant.   (3)

The need for transport in animals: circulation

Key points ⚠

1 In mammals nutrients, oxygen and carbon dioxide are transported in the blood. ☐
2 Blood is pumped by a four-chambered **heart**. ☐
3 Blood is pumped from the heart to the **lungs** then back to the heart before being pumped to all other parts of the body. ☐
4 Two chambers called the left and right **ventricles** pump blood out of the heart and into **arteries**. ☐
5 The arteries carrying blood away from the heart to the lungs are the **pulmonary arteries**. ☐
6 The artery carrying blood away from the heart and which branches to all other parts of the body is the **aorta**. ☐
7 Branches of the aorta that supply the heart muscle itself with blood are the **coronary** arteries. ☐
8 Two chambers called the left and right **atria** receive blood into the heart from **veins**. ☐
9 Veins bringing blood to the heart from the lungs are the **pulmonary veins**. ☐
10 Veins bringing blood to the heart from all parts of the body join to form the **vena cava** before entering the heart. ☐
11 Arteries carry blood away from the heart and have thick, muscular walls and a relatively narrow internal diameter. ☐
12 Blood in arteries is under high pressure. ☐
13 Veins carry blood back to the heart and have thinner walls and relatively wider internal diameters than similar-sized arteries. ☐
14 Blood in veins is under lower pressure than blood in the arteries. ☐
15 To prevent the low-pressure blood from flowing backwards, veins have **valves**. ☐
16 Within organs and tissues, blood is carried in networks of **capillaries**. Capillaries link the arteries supplying the organ or tissue with the veins, which carry the blood away from the organ or tissue. ☐
17 Capillaries have thin walls and their networks produce a large surface area through which material can be exchanged with tissues efficiently. ☐
18 **Red blood cells** are specialised because they have **haemoglobin**, a red oxygen-carrying pigment. ☐

Summary notes

Animal transport systems

In mammals, oxygen, carbon dioxide, nutrients such as glucose, wastes and other substances are transported in the blood, which circulates round their bodies – see the table on page 75.

Substance transported	Transport route
Nutrients	Small intestine to all cells
Nitrogenous wastes	All cells to kidneys
Oxygen	Lungs to all cells
Carbon dioxide	All cells to lungs
Hormones	Glands to target organs

Pathway of blood in circulation

The circulatory system consists of the heart, blood vessels and the blood they contain.

The human circulatory system is a double circulation where the blood flows twice through the heart for each complete circuit. The lungs have a separate circulation from the rest of the body, which increases the efficiency because oxygenated blood can be kept separate from deoxygenated blood. Figure 2.21 shows the pathway of blood through the heart, lungs and body.

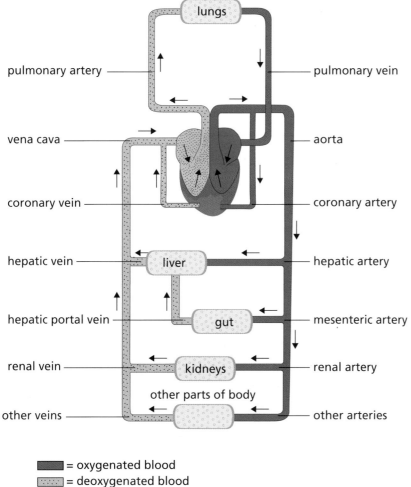

■ = oxygenated blood
▨ = deoxygenated blood
▧ = capillary bed

Figure 2.21 Pathway of blood through the heart, lungs and body

Blood vessels

There are three main types of blood vessel in the circulatory system of a mammal, each with distinct features and functions. This is summarised in the table on page 76.

the table on page 76.

Hints & tips

A for Artery, A for Away
V for Veins, V for Valves;
veIN to the heart
CaPillArieS let substances
PASs through their thin
walls

Type of blood vessel	Function	Features
Arteries narrow internal diameter thick muscular layer	Carry blood away from the heart	Thick muscular wall Pulse can be detected Blood at high pressure
Capillaries thin wall (one cell thick)	Carry blood through tissues and organs Exchange of materials	Thin wall, one cell thick
Veins wide internal diameter valve thin muscular layer	Carry blood towards the heart	Thin muscular wall No pulse detected Blood at low pressure Contains valves

Circulation

When an artery from the heart reaches an organ it divides up into a network of very narrow capillaries. The capillaries join up into a vein to carry blood out of the organ and back to the heart. The capillaries within an organ create a large surface area in contact with the cells of the organ. This allows efficient exchange of materials between the cells of the organ and the bloodstream.

Heart structure

The heart is a muscular pump, which has four chambers. There are two atria (top chambers of the heart), the right atrium and the left atrium, and two ventricles (bottom chambers of the heart), the right ventricle and the left ventricle. The heart has four valves, which prevent the backflow of blood, so that blood flows in one direction only.

Major blood vessels carry blood into and out of the heart. The main veins return blood under low pressure and the main arteries take blood under high pressure out of the heart.

Pathway of blood through the heart

Deoxygenated blood from the body returns to the heart in the vena cava. It enters the right atrium and is then pumped through a valve into the right ventricle. The right ventricle then pumps the deoxygenated blood through another valve and out through the pulmonary artery to the lungs where it picks up oxygen.

> **Hints & tips** ★
>
> *Arteries and veins are like motorways between cities carrying quantities of goods and transporting waste materials. The capillaries are like the busy streets within the city where loading and unloading of the goods and waste materials take place.*

Oxygenated blood from the lungs returns to the heart in the pulmonary vein. It enters the left atrium and is pumped through a valve into the left ventricle. The thick cardiac muscle of the left ventricle then pumps the oxygenated blood through another valve and out through the aorta to the body. Figure 2.22 shows a section through the heart with its main blood vessels and the pathway of blood through it.

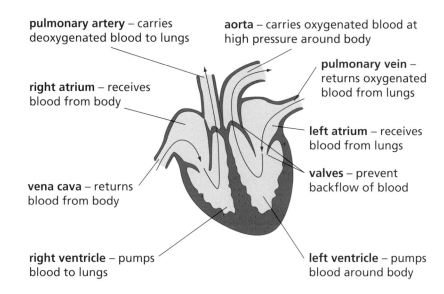

pulmonary artery – carries deoxygenated blood to lungs

aorta – carries oxygenated blood at high pressure around body

pulmonary vein – returns oxygenated blood from lungs

right atrium – receives blood from body

left atrium – receives blood from lungs

vena cava – returns blood from body

valves – prevent backflow of blood

right ventricle – pumps blood to lungs

left ventricle – pumps blood around body

Figure 2.22 Structure of the heart and main blood vessels

The coronary blood vessels

The heart muscle requires its own blood supply to provide it with oxygen and glucose for respiration. This is provided by the coronary blood vessels, which can be seen on the outside of the heart in Figure 2.23. The coronary arteries branch off the aorta and carry oxygenated blood to the heart muscle. The coronary veins carry the deoxygenated blood away and connect to the vena cava. Heart disease results if the coronary arteries become narrow or blocked. A heart attack occurs when a coronary vessel becomes blocked. The region of the heart muscle it supplies is starved of oxygen and dies. If only a small area of heart muscle dies, a mild heart attack occurs and the person may recover fully. If a large area of heart muscle dies, a severe heart attack occurs and the person may die. There is more about the causes of blocked coronary arteries in Key Area 2.7.

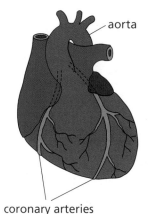

aorta

coronary arteries

Figure 2.23 Coronary blood supply

Pulse

Each time the heart muscle contracts, a small volume of blood is pumped at high pressure into the arteries. This produces a wave of pressure that can be felt as a pulse beat in an artery, especially where the artery comes near to the surface of the body, for example at the wrist.

Blood

Blood is composed mainly of plasma – a watery, yellow liquid in which blood cells float. There are several types of cell in blood including red blood cells, which give the blood its colour. Figure 2.24 shows a diagram of a red blood cell.

Red blood cells:

- are very small
- are very numerous
- are filled with the red pigment called haemoglobin
- have no nucleus, which gives more space for haemoglobin
- have a flattened disc shape to increase surface area for gas exchange
- are flexible and so can squeeze through tiny capillaries

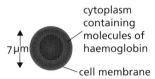

Figure 2.24 Red blood cell

The transport of oxygen

Red blood cells are specialised to carry oxygen attached to a protein called haemoglobin. Haemoglobin can rapidly combine with oxygen in the highly oxygenated environment of the lungs. Haemoglobin can rapidly release oxygen in the poorly oxygenated environment of other tissues. This is shown in the following equation:

$$\text{haemoglobin} + \text{oxygen} \underset{\text{in the tissues}}{\overset{\text{in the lungs}}{\rightleftharpoons}} \text{oxyhaemoglobin}$$

Key words

Aorta – main artery that carries oxygenated blood away from the heart in mammals
Artery – general name for a blood vessel that carries blood away from the heart
Atria – upper chambers of the heart, which receive blood from veins (*sing.* atrium)
Capillaries – tiny blood vessels with walls one-cell thick where exchange of materials occurs
Coronary – referring to the heart and the blood vessels that serve the heart tissues
Haemoglobin – pigment in red blood cells that transports oxygen as oxyhaemoglobin
Heart – muscular organ that pumps blood around the body
Pulmonary artery – artery carrying deoxygenated blood from the heart to the lungs
Pulmonary vein – vein carrying oxygenated blood to the heart from the lungs
Red blood cell – blood cell containing the pigment haemoglobin responsible for the transport of oxygen
Valve – structure in veins that prevents the backflow of blood
Vein – general name for a blood vessel with valves that transports blood to the heart
Vena cava – vein carrying deoxygenated blood to the heart from the body systems
Ventricles – lower chambers of the heart that receive blood from the atria and pump it into arteries

Questions

A Restricted-response questions (1 mark each)

1 State the function of the heart.
2 Name the **four** chambers of the heart.
3 Name the following blood vessels:
   a) vein that returns deoxygenated blood from the body to the heart

$\Rightarrow$

⇨
b) artery that transports deoxygenated blood from the heart to the lungs
c) vein that transports oxygenated blood from the lungs to the heart
d) artery that transports oxygenated blood from the heart to the body
4 State the general role of valves.
5 Name the artery that supplies the cardiac muscle of the heart with blood.
6 Name the following blood vessels:
a) artery that supplies the liver with blood from the heart
b) artery that supplies the kidney with blood from the heart
c) vein that transports blood from the small intestine to the liver
7 Name the red-coloured substance in blood and state its function.

B Extended-response questions (2 or 3 marks)

1 Use the information in Figure 2.21 to explain the differences between the muscular wall of the left ventricle and the wall of the right ventricle. (2)
2 Describe the general functions of the following blood vessel types:
a) arteries
b) veins
c) capillaries (3)
3 Explain how the structure of red blood cells helps them carry out their function. (3)

The need for transport in animals: gas exchange and nutrient absorption

Key points !

1 Airways that link the atmosphere with gas exchange surfaces within the lungs are kept open with rings of **cartilage**. ☐

2 Most of the main airways are lined with sticky **mucus**, which traps dirt particles and microorganisms, preventing these from reaching the gas exchange surface. ☐

3 The mucus and trapped material in the airways are swept out of the lungs by the movement of small hairs called **cilia**. ☐

4 The gas exchange surfaces are composed of thin-walled sacs called **alveoli**. ☐

5 Alveoli have a rich blood supply and form a large surface area for efficient gas exchange. ☐

6 Oxygen and carbon dioxide are exchanged by diffusion between the air and the blood through the thin walls of the alveoli. ☐

7 Swallowed food is moved through the digestive system by a muscular action called peristalsis. ☐

8 Digested food is absorbed through the small intestine wall and into the blood and **lymph**. ☐

9 The small intestine wall has thin-walled folds called **villi**, which increase its surface area for absorption of digested food. ☐

10 Each villus has a good blood supply and a central lymph vessel called a **lacteal**. ☐

11 Glucose and amino acids are absorbed directly into the bloodstream and the products of fat digestion pass into the lacteals. ☐

12 Lacteals lead into the lymphatic system. ☐

Summary notes

Gas exchange

The lungs

The lungs (Figure 2.25) are where the gases oxygen and carbon dioxide are exchanged between the blood and the air.

The trachea and bronchi have C-shaped rings of cartilage, which keep the airways open. The trachea is lined with sticky mucus to trap dirt particles and microorganisms from inhaled air. The sticky lining has cells with hair-like cilia, which beat to sweep the mucus and trapped material up and out of the lungs (Figure 2.26).

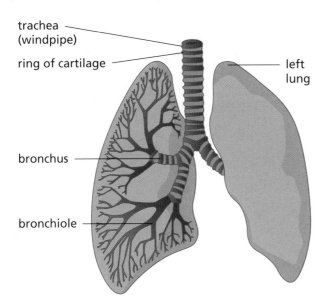

Figure 2.25 The lungs in the chest cavity

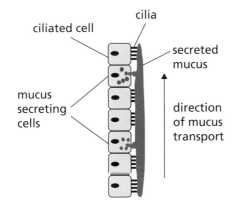

Figure 2.26 Lining of the trachea

Clean inhaled air passes down the trachea, bronchi and bronchioles and finally reaches the tiny alveoli, which make up the gas exchange surface. Oxygen from the air dissolves in the moist surface layer lining the alveoli. It diffuses rapidly into the red blood cells through the single-celled walls of the alveoli and blood capillaries. Carbon dioxide diffuses out of the blood and into the air in the alveoli (Figure 2.27). Exhaled air passes out of the lungs.

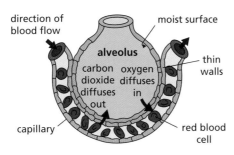

Figure 2.27 Gas exchange at an alveolus

Efficiency of the gas exchange surface

The internal structure of the lungs has many features that promote diffusion of gases and make gas exchange efficient. These are outlined in the table on the next page.

Feature	Provided by...
Large surface area	...many alveoli in contact with a branching capillary network
Good blood supply	...a large branching capillary network
Very thin walls	...the single-celled walls of the alveoli and capillaries
Moist surfaces	...the fluid lining the alveoli

Nutrition

Food groups

The main food groups in the human diet are carbohydrates, fats, proteins, vitamins and minerals.

Carbohydrates are energy rich and are used to provide energy for cellular processes such as mitosis and synthesis of large molecules. Examples of carbohydrates include sugars, starch and cellulose. Foods rich in carbohydrate include bread, potatoes, pasta and rice. Carbohydrates can be simple sugars or more complex molecules consisting of many simple sugars joined together.

Fats are an energy source and when stored under the skin help insulate animals. Foods rich in fats include butter and olive oil. The basic units used to build fats are glycerol and fatty acids. Three fatty acid molecules are joined together to each glycerol molecule.

Proteins are required for growth and repair of tissues. Foods rich in protein include meat, cheese, fish and nuts. The basic units used to build proteins are called amino acids. There are about 20 different types of amino acid. Proteins can be made of several hundred amino acids joined together. The sequence of the amino acids determines the type of protein.

The need for digestion

Many of the large carbohydrate, fat and protein molecules present in the food that we eat are insoluble. Digestion involves the breakdown of large, insoluble food molecules into small, soluble molecules by enzymes. This is required because only soluble molecules can pass through the wall of the small intestine and enter the blood. Substances must be soluble so that they can first dissolve, which then allows them to diffuse through the small intestine and into the blood.

Hints & tips

Remember DD: Dissolve to Diffuse

Function of the digestive system

The alimentary canal is a long, muscular tube that runs from the mouth to the anus. As food travels through the alimentary canal digestion takes place. Figure 2.28 shows the main features of the digestive system.

Peristalsis

Food is moved along the digestive system by a muscular process called peristalsis. Muscles in the wall of the digestive system contract behind the ball of food to squeeze the food along. Circular muscles in front of the food relax to allow the food to move easily (Figure 2.29).

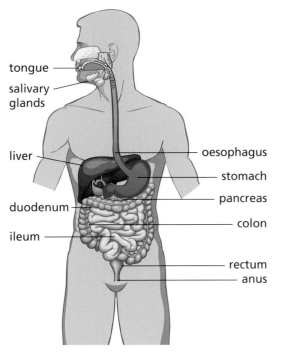

Figure 2.28 Digestive system in humans

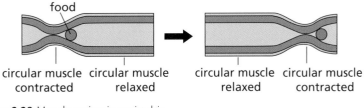

Figure 2.29 Muscle action in peristalsis

Peristalsis takes place throughout the alimentary canal.

The small intestine and absorption

Soluble molecules produced by digestion pass through the small intestine wall by diffusion and enter the bloodstream and lymph system.

The structure of the small intestine allows very efficient absorption to take place. It is long and the inner lining is folded and has many finger-like projections called villi (Figure 2.30), which increase the surface area available for the absorption of the soluble food molecules. The surface is moist so that molecules can dissolve before diffusing.

The features of the villi lining the small intestine that promote efficient absorption are outlined in the table below.

Feature of the villi	Advantage
The thin wall is one cell thick	Allows dissolved molecules to pass through quickly and easily by rapid diffusion
Branching blood capillary present	Ensures a good blood supply is present to receive and transport absorbed glucose and amino acid molecules
Central lacteal present	Ensures that products of fat digestion can be absorbed and passed to the lymph system

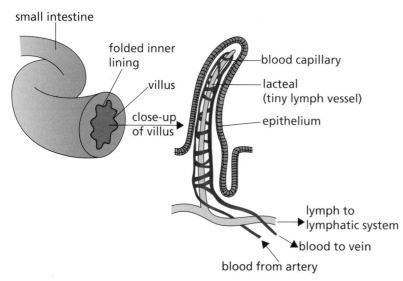

small intestine

folded inner lining

villus

close-up of villus

blood capillary

lacteal (tiny lymph vessel)

epithelium

lymph to lymphatic system

blood to vein

blood from artery

Figure 2.30 Villi lining the small intestine and structure of a single villus

Key words

Alveoli – tiny sacs in lungs that form the gas exchange surface (*sing.* alveolus)

Cartilage – flexible tissue forming C-shaped rings in the trachea to keep the airway open

Cilia – hair-like structures lining the trachea that move mucus with trapped bacteria away from the lungs (*sing.* cilium)

Digestion – breakdown of large, insoluble food molecules into smaller, soluble ones

Lacteal – central vessel in the villi responsible for the absorption of fats

Lungs – organs responsible for gas exchange in mammals, birds, reptiles and amphibians

Lymph – liquid that circulates within a mammal's body, transporting the products of fat digestion from the lacteals

Mucus – sticky substance lining the trachea and bronchi, trapping dust and bacteria

Peristalsis – waves of muscular contraction responsible for the movement of food through the intestines

Villi – finger-like projections of the small intestine lining providing a large surface area for absorption of food (*sing.* villus)

Questions ?

A Restricted-response questions (1 mark each)

1 State the function of the rings of cartilage around the main airways.
2 Give **three** features of alveoli that allow efficient gas exchange.
3 Name the finger-like projections that line the inside of the small intestine.
4 State how glucose and amino acids are absorbed by the villi.
5 State how the products of fat digestion are absorbed by the villi.
6 State how glucose and amino acids are transported around the body.
7 State how the products of fat digestion are transported around the body.

B Extended-response questions (2 or 3 marks)

1 Describe the role of the mucus and cilia in the main airways.   (2)
2 Describe the action of peristalsis.   (2)
3 Describe the similarities in the structure and function of the alveoli and the villi. (3)

Effects of lifestyle choices on human transport and exchange systems

Key points !

1. A **lifestyle choice** refers to options that a human might have, related to their daily living patterns. ☐
2. Certain lifestyle choices have the potential to affect an individual's circulatory and exchange systems. ☐
3. Diet is a lifestyle choice. ☐
4. Exercise level is a lifestyle choice. ☐
5. Use of tobacco is a lifestyle choice. ☐
6. Use of alcohol is a lifestyle choice. ☐
7. High-stress experiences can impact on health. ☐
8. Individuals have the responsibility for their own awareness of the effects of lifestyle options when making personal choices. ☐

Summary notes

The factors related to lifestyle choice have been grouped under the headings shown below. However, many of the effects described are the results of combinations of these factors and many of the issues raised here are very relevant to the situation in modern Scotland.

Diet

Overeating, high intake of saturated fat and excessive sugar and salt intake are examples of diet issues that can lead to health problems. Obesity is the presence of excessive body fat and a major factor causing it is overeating. Obesity can increase the risk of heart disease and type 2 diabetes.

Foods that are high in saturated fat increase the levels of cholesterol in the blood. Cholesterol is a substance that can be deposited in the arteries, producing blockages. These lead to narrowing of the arteries, making it more difficult for blood to flow through them. If a blockage ruptures, a blood clot can form. If a blood clot blocks the coronary arteries to the heart muscle a heart attack can result. If a blood clot occurs in the brain, a stroke can result.

Blood pressure is the force of the blood pushing against the walls of the arteries. High blood pressure puts extra strain on the heart and blood vessels. People with high blood pressure are at an increased risk of suffering a heart attack or stroke. High blood pressure can result due to narrowing of the arteries caused by a diet high in saturated fat, too much salt in the diet and obesity. This results in the heart having to work harder to pump blood around the body, which can damage the heart and blood vessels.

Effect of exercise

It is important to have an active lifestyle and to take regular exercise. Exercise improves the blood flow to muscles and improves circulation. By exercising regularly and maintaining a healthy body weight the risks of heart disease, strokes, high blood pressure and type 2 diabetes are greatly reduced.

Use of tobacco

Smoking increases the risk of developing heart disease. Nicotine is an addictive substance in cigarette smoke. Its stimulant properties also increase the blood pressure. Many of the chemicals found in cigarette smoke are known to be carcinogenic. This means that they can cause cancer. Tar in cigarette smoke enters the lungs and damages the cilia lining the trachea, reducing their ability to protect the lungs from damage and infection. Inhaled smoke also contains carbon monoxide. This gas combines with the haemoglobin in red blood cells and so reduces the ability of the red blood cells to transport oxygen around the body. Carbon monoxide also increases blood pressure.

Use of alcohol

Heavy drinking can result in an increase in blood pressure, which increases the risk of a heart attack or stroke. It can also trigger type 2 diabetes. Drinking large quantities of alcohol over a long period of time can lead to liver damage and a condition called cirrhosis. Cirrhosis is the irreversible scarring of the liver. Eventually the liver stops working and a transplant is required.

Stress

Although stress is not a confirmed risk factor for either high blood pressure or heart disease, scientists continue to study how stress relates to our health. While blood pressure may increase temporarily when the body is under stress, it has not been proven to cause long-term high blood pressure. Some people cope with stress by overeating or eating unhealthy foods, smoking, drinking and other activities that do raise their risk of heart attack, stroke and high blood pressure. Being under stress is not necessarily a lifestyle choice an individual has made, and might be the result of unavoidable circumstances in life.

Lifestyle choice and the NHS

In recent years, a debate has started about whether there should be free national health treatment for all illnesses as there is at present. What do you think? Should smokers receive free treatment for lung cancer? Should obese individuals have free treatment for diabetes?

Key words

Lifestyle choice – decisions on lifestyle that impact on an individual's health

Questions ?

A Restricted-response questions (1 mark each)

1 Give **three** examples of lifestyle choices that can result in health problems.
2 State what is meant by the term obesity.
3 State what is meant by the phrase high blood pressure.

B Extended-response questions (2 or 3 marks)

1 Give **two** examples of how stress can lead indirectly to health problems.   (2)
2 Describe health problems that can be linked with any **three** of the following lifestyle choices:
   - high saturated fat in the diet
   - high salt in the diet
   - lack of exercise
   - use of tobacco
   - abuse of alcohol   (3)

Answers

Key Area 2.1

A Restricted-response questions (1 mark each)

1 tissue
2 a) mesophyll, epidermis, xylem, phloem, cambium…(*other possible answers*)   [any 1]
   b) blood, muscle, nervous…(*other possible answers*)   [any 1]
3 group of tissues working together
4 a) leaf, stem, root, flower, fruit…(*other possible answers*)   [any 1]
   b) brain, heart, kidney…(*other possible answers*)   [any 1]
5 group of organs working together
6 nervous, circulatory, respiratory, digestive, excretory, reproductive, skeletal…(*other possible answers*)   [any 3]
7 senses the environment, processes information, responds to the environment
8 produces gametes, allows development of offspring
9 transports foods, transports oxygen, transports wastes, assists in defence

B Extended-response questions (2 or 3 marks)

1 cells change structure; to allow them to carry out a particular function   [1 each = 2]
2 cells of the body are organised into tissues; tissues have particular functions; tissues are organised into organs; organs work together in systems; systems are coordinated to allow survival of the organism   [any 3 = 3]

Answers

Key Area 2.2

A Restricted-response questions (1 mark each)

1 structure suited to function
2 divide to produce a supply of cells that can then specialise
3 bone cell, muscle cell, skin cell, blood cell … (other possible answers)   [any 1]
4 meristems
5 shoot tip, root tip, vascular tissues in stem or root   [any 1]
6 epidermal, mesophyll … (other possible answers)   [any 2]

B Extended-response questions (2 or 3 marks)

1 cell division; loses nucleus; develops haemoglobin; becomes dimpled   [any 2 = 2]
2 similarity – each can divide, both non-specialised; difference – embryonic can become any cell, adult more limited   [1 each = 3]
3 moral principle to improve medicine; moral principle to respect human life; the two principles cannot both be respected in embryonic stem cell research   [1 each = 3]

Answers

Key Area 2.3a

A Restricted-response questions (1 mark each)

1 brain and spinal cord   [both]
2 as electrical impulses
3 linked at synapses
4 convert stimuli to electrical impulses
5 protection

B Extended-response questions (2 or 3 marks)

1 accepts information; processes information; responds to information   [all 3 = 2, 2/1 = 1]
2 a) reasoning, memory, emotions, others
   b) balance, coordination of movement
   c) control of heart rate, breathing rate and peristalsis   [all 3 = 2, 2/1 = 1]
3 a) carry electrical impulses to CNS
   b) transmit electrical impulses from sensory neurons to motor neurons
   c) transmit electrical impulses to the effectors   [all 3 = 2, 2/1 = 1]
4 transmitter molecules are released into gap at synapse; receptors of the next neuron are affected; electrical impulse moves on   [all 3 = 2, 2/1 = 1]
5 stimuli affect receptors; electrical impulses pass through sensory neurons; processed by relay neurons in spinal cord; electrical impulses sent to effectors; effectors make response   [any 3 = 3]

Answers

Key Area 2.3b

A Restricted-response questions (1 mark each)

1 produce and secrete hormones into the bloodstream
2 pancreas, adrenal, pituitary…(other possible answers) [any 2]
3 dissolved in the bloodstream
4 target cells
5 insulin, glucagon, adrenaline [any 2]

6 increased life expectancy; increased consumption of sugar; increase in sedentary lifestyles; increased obesity [any 1]

B Extended-response questions (2 or 3 marks)

1 each hormone has a function not carried out by any others; affects only the receptors on its target organ [1 each = 2]

2 produces insulin, which causes excess blood glucose to be stored; produces glucagon, which causes release of glucose from store [1 each = 2]
3 stores excess glucose as glycogen; releases glucose from glycogen [1 each = 2]
4 raised glucose triggers insulin release by pancreas; insulin causes liver to convert glucose to glycogen and store it; when glucose levels fall glucagon released by pancreas; glucagon converts glycogen to glucose [any 3 = 3]
5 type 1 appears in childhood; caused by lack of insulin; type 2 often appears in overweight individuals; caused by liver receptors not responding to insulin

Answers

Key Area 2.4

A Restricted-response questions (1 mark each)

1 a) one set of chromosomes in the nucleus
  b) two sets of chromosomes in the nucleus [both]
2 male – anthers, female – ovaries [both]
3 male – pollen, female – ovules [both]
4 male – testes, female – ovaries [both]
5 male – sperm, female – ova [both]
6 fusion of male and female gamete nuclei
7 gametes haploid so that fertilisation restores the diploid state

8 zygote
9 mitosis

B Extended-response questions (2 or 3 marks)

1 Sperm cells are tiny and have a tail for swimming; ova are large and have a food supply to feed the early embryo [1 each = 2]
2 male pollen carried from anthers by wind or insects; pollen arrives on female parts of flower; pollen grows through female tissue to reach the ovary; pollen nucleus fuses with female ovule nucleus [any 3 = 3]

Answers

Key Area 2.5

A Restricted-response questions (1 mark each)

1 variation
2 a) variation that shows a range of differences
  b) variation in which the values are clear-cut [both]
3 height, weight...(*other possible answers*) [any 2]
4 blood group, eye colour...(*other possible answers*) [any 2]
5 controlled by the activity of a group of genes
6 1 chance in 4 or 25% chance [either]

B Extended-response questions (2 or 3 marks)

1 gene codes for a characteristic; allele is a form of a gene [1 each = 2]

2 genotype – statement of alleles of individual; phenotype – outward appearance of individual [1 each = 2]
3 homozygous – having two alleles the same; heterozygous – having two different alleles [1 each = 2]
4 dominant alleles always show in the phenotype; recessive alleles only show in phenotype when homozygous [1 each = 2]
5 4 Cc, 7 cc [1 each = 2]
6 variation is differences between members of a species; variation is mostly genetic and can be inherited; natural selection acts on variation; result of natural selection is evolution [any 3 = 3]

Answers

Key Area 2.6a

A Restricted-response questions (1 mark each)

1 transport water to leaves for photosynthesis; transport food around plant [both]
2 sugar, water, minerals [any 2]
3 narrow, hollow, tube-shaped; walls of lignin [both]
4 conduct water up from roots towards stems and leaves
5 transpiration
6 can change shape to open and close the stomata, so controlling gas exchange
7 transport sugars around the plant

B Extended-response questions (2 or 3 marks)

1 photosynthesis; transport of substances; support for plant; cooling effect of transpiration [3 = 2, 2/1 = 1]
2 water uptake by osmosis; root hair cells increase the surface area of root epidermis [1 each = 2]
3 loses water by evaporation to leaf air spaces; lowers water concentration in mesophyll cells; allows water to be drawn into mesophyll from xylem by osmosis [3 = 2, 2/1 = 1]
4 water taken into roots by osmosis; water passes up xylem; water drawn into leaf by osmosis; water evaporates into air spaces in leaf; water moves out of leaf to air through stomata [all 5 = 3, 4/3 = 2, 2 = 1]

Answers

Key Area 2.6b

A Restricted-response questions (1 mark each)

1 pumps blood around body
2 right and left atria, right and left ventricles [all 4]
3 a) vena cava
   b) pulmonary artery
   c) pulmonary vein
   d) aorta [all 4]
4 prevent backflow of blood
5 coronary artery
6 a) hepatic artery
   b) renal artery
   c) hepatic portal vein [all 3]
7 haemoglobin; carries oxygen [both]

B Extended-response questions (2 or 3 marks)

1 left ventricle has a thicker muscular wall than the right; left has to pump blood around the whole body and right ventricle only pumps blood to the lungs [1 each = 2]
2 a) arteries carry blood from the heart to the organs
   b) veins return blood to the heart from the organs
   c) capillaries exchange substances with tissues [1 each = 3]
3 red blood cells have no nucleus which gives extra space inside; they are very small with dimples on each side, which increases their surface area for gas exchange; they contain haemoglobin, which carries oxygen [1 each = 3]

Answers

Key Area 2.6c

A Restricted-response questions (1 mark each)

1 keep airways open
2 large surface area, good blood supply, thin walls [all 3]
3 villi
4 taken directly into blood in capillaries
5 taken directly into the lacteal
6 carried in the bloodstream
7 carried in the lymphatic system

B Extended-response questions (2 or 3 marks)

1 mucus traps particles; cilia beat and sweep mucus up and out of the breathing system [1 each = 2]
2 circular muscles relax in front of food; circular muscles contract behind the food and push it along [1 each = 2]
3 both have large surface area; thin walls; moist walls; good blood supply [1 each = 3]

Answers

Key Area 2.7

A Restricted-response questions (1 mark each)

1 high fat/salt/sugar diet, insufficient exercise, smoking, excessive alcohol intake [any 3]
2 high levels of body fat related to excessive food intake
3 blood forced excessively against walls of blood vessels

B Extended-response questions (2 or 3 marks)

1 can lead to overeating or eating unhealthy foods/smoking/drinking alcohol; can lead to heart attack/stroke/high blood pressure/diabetes
2 • obesity, high cholesterol levels
   • raised blood pressure
   • obesity, artery blockage, diabetes
   • heart disease, cancers
   • liver disease

Practice assessment: Unit 2 (40 marks)

Section A (10 marks)

1   The diagram below shows a single neuron.

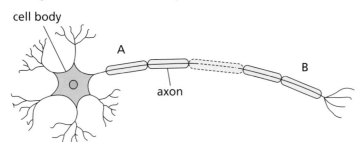

Which line in the table below correctly identifies this type of neuron and the direction of electrical impulse along its fibre?

	Type of neuron	Direction of impulse
A	Sensory	A → B
B	Motor	B → A
C	Sensory	B → A
D	Motor	A → B

2   Which of the following terms refers to variation in which there are clear-cut differences?

A   continuous

B   polygenic

C   discrete

D   heterozygous

3   Which line in the table below correctly describes phloem cells?

	Description of cell walls	Substance(s) transported
A	Lignified	Water and minerals
B	Lignified	Sugars
C	Non-lignified	Sugars
D	Non-lignified	Water and minerals

4   Which line in the table below correctly describes arteries and veins?

	Arteries	Veins
A	Low pressure	Wide internal diameter
B	High pressure	Wide internal diameter
C	Low pressure	Narrow internal diameter
D	High pressure	Narrow internal diameter

5   Which structures form part of the lungs and contain gases which are exchanged between the air and the bloodstream?

A   villi

B   alveoli

C   capillaries

D   cilia

Questions 6 and 7 refer to the diagram below, which shows part of the human digestive system.

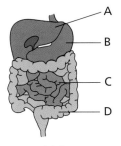

A

B

C

D

6 In which structure would lacteals be found?

7 In which structure would peristalsis **not** occur?

Questions 8 and 9 refer to the graph below, which shows how increasing the percentage of carbon dioxide in the air affects the volume of air inhaled each minute.

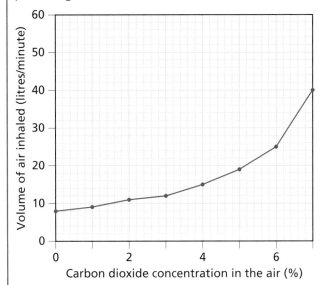

Carbon dioxide concentration in the air (%)

Volume of air inhaled (litres/minute)

8 The volume of carbon dioxide entering the lungs each minute when the carbon dioxide concentration in the air is 7% is:

A 2.8 litres   B 17.5 litres   C 28.0 litres   D 40.0 litres

9 When the carbon dioxide concentration of the air is increased from 2% to 5%, the volume of air inhaled increases by:

A 6 litres per minute   B 8 litres per minute   C 10 litres per minute   D 19 litres per minute

10 The graph below shows how the percentage saturation of haemoglobin changes as the concentration of oxygen in the fluid surrounding it increases.

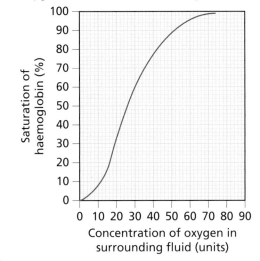

Concentration of oxygen in surrounding fluid (units)

Saturation of haemoglobin (%)

93

⇨
Which of the following conclusions can be drawn from the graph?

A As the oxygen concentration in the surrounding fluid increases, the percentage saturation of haemoglobin increases steadily.

B The highest percentage saturation of haemoglobin occurs when oxygen concentration is lowest.

C The rate of increase in percentage saturation of haemoglobin decreases at the highest oxygen concentrations.

D The lowest oxygen concentrations stimulate the most rapid increase in percentage saturation of haemoglobin.

Section B (30 marks)

1 The statements in the table below relate to the cells of a multicellular organism.
Copy the table and then decide if each statement is true or false and tick the appropriate box. If you decide that the statement is false write the correct word into the correction box to replace the word underlined in the statement. (3)

Statement	True	False	Correction
Similar cells with the same function are grouped into <u>organs</u> in multicellular organisms			
Stem cells are <u>specialised</u> cells in animals that can divide and become different types of cell			
In plants, non-specialised cells are produced in regions called <u>meristems</u>			

2 The diagram shows part of the human central nervous system (CNS).

a) Name part X. (1)

b) Copy the table below, which shows the results of direct damage to various parts of the brain. Predict the part of the brain that is most likely to have been damaged in each case and add the information to the table. (3)

Part of brain damaged	Result
	Ability to balance impaired
	Loss of ability to control heart rate
	Reduced ability to remember simple experiences

X

3 The diagram below shows a section through a sweet pea flower.

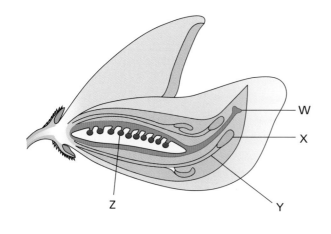

W

X

Z

Y

⇨

⇨

    a) Identify the letter that shows the site of production of male gametes in this flower. (1)

    b) Copy the sentence below, choosing the correct term from the choice in brackets to make it correct. (2)

       The female gametes of a flowering plant are found within the (ovaries/stamens) and have the (diploid/haploid) number of chromosomes.

4 The diagram below shows part of the experimental apparatus used to investigate the effect of increasing temperature on transpiration rate in a young plant seedling.

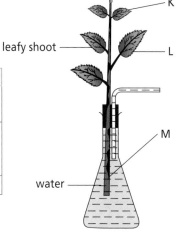

    a) Copy and complete the table below, which refers to the location of various structures labelled on the diagram. (3)

Letter	Name of structure	Function in transport
K		Allow water vapour to escape out of the leaf to the atmosphere
L		Have air spaces between cells into which water can evaporate before passing out of leaf
M	Xylem vessels	

    b) The table below shows how the transpiration rate from the leaves of this plant varied as the temperature was raised during the experiment.

Temperature (°C)	Transpiration rate (cm³ water per hour per cm² leaf surface)
10	2.4
20	4.6
30	10.2
40	10.8

       (i) On a piece of graph paper, plot a line graph of these data to show temperature against the transpiration rate. (2SSI)

      (ii) Give **two** variables that must be kept constant at each temperature to ensure that a valid conclusion could be drawn using the results of this experiment. (1SSI)

     (iii) Calculate the average rate of transpiration over the temperatures tested. (1SSI)

     (iv) Using the data in the table, give the expected transpiration rate of this plant at 35°C. (1SSI)

5 The table below shows some terms involved in the description of variation and inheritance in living organisms. Copy and complete the table by adding the missing term and descriptions. (2)

Term	Description
Genotype	
	An organism with two identical alleles of a particular gene

6 The diagram on p. 96 shows a plan of the basic circulatory system of a mammal.

    a) Name the chamber of the heart that pumps blood into vessel B. (1)

    b) Name blood vessel F. (1)

    c) Describe why vessels such as E have valves. (1)

    d) Give a letter on the circulation plan that shows where a capillary blood vessel could be found. (1)

⇨

⇨

7 Mucus and cilia are involved in the cleaning mechanism of the lungs. Describe the roles that each of these plays in keeping the gas exchange surface clean. (2)

8 Give an account of how a rise in blood glucose concentration in humans is controlled. (2)

9 Choose one of the following lifestyle options:
- ○ Eating a diet low in saturated fat, sugar and salt.
- ○ Opting not to smoke.
- ○ Taking regular, high-intensity exercise.

Explain why your chosen option has potential health benefits. (2)

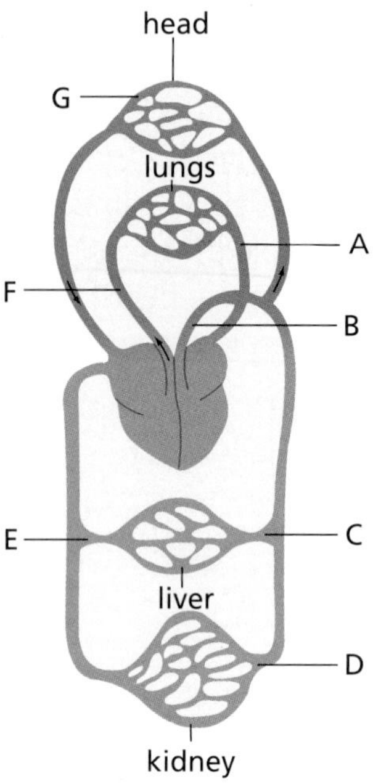

Diagram labels: head, G, lungs, A, F, B, E, C, liver, D, kidney

Answers to practice assessment: Unit 2

Section A

1 D, 2 C, 3 C, 4 B, 5 B, 6 C, 7 A, 8 A, 9 B, 10 C

Section B

1 false – tissues
  false – non-specialised or unspecialised
  true   [1 per correct line]

2 a) spinal cord
  b) cerebellum
     medulla
     cerebrum   [1 per correct line]

3 a) X
  b) ovaries, haploid   [1 each]

4 a) K stomata
     L spongy mesophyll
     M carry water and minerals up stem to leaves   [1 each]
  b) (i) scales and labels   [1]
         plots and joining   [1]
     (ii) light intensity, air movements, size of seedling, humidity   [any 2]
     (iii) 7.0 cm³ per hr per cm²
     (iv) 10.4–10.5 cm³ per hr per cm²

5 statement of the different alleles of a gene an individual has
  homozygous   [1 per correct line]

6 a) left ventricle
  b) pulmonary artery
  c) prevent backflow of blood
  d) G

7 mucus – traps breathed-in particles and microorganisms
  cilia – beat and sweep mucus out of lungs and airways

8 rise detected by receptors in the pancreas; pancreas releases insulin; insulin causes conversion of excess glucose to glycogen in the liver   [all 3 = 2, 2/1 = 1]

9 healthy diet – reduces risk of obesity, stroke, type 2 diabetes
  not smoking – reduces risk of cancers, stroke, heart disease
  exercise – reduces risk of obesity, stroke, diabetes, heart disease   [in each option 3 = 2, 2/1 = 1]

Life on Earth

Biodiversity and the distribution of life

Key points ❗

1. **Biodiversity** in **ecosystems** is affected by **abiotic** and **biotic** factors. ☐
2. Abiotic factors are physical factors and include temperature and pH. ☐
3. Biotic factors are related directly to living organisms and include factors such as **grazing** and **predation**. ☐
4. Humans can influence biodiversity in ecosystems through creation of **pollution**, **habitat destruction** and **overexploitation** of species. ☐
5. A **biome** is a geographical region of the planet that is characterised by its climate and contains distinctive communities of plants (**flora**) and animals (**fauna**). ☐
6. The global occurrence of particular biomes depends on the physical characteristics of the area, including the climatic factors of temperature and **precipitation** (rainfall). ☐
7. An ecosystem is the **community** of organisms living in a **habitat** and their interactions with the non-living components of the system. ☐
8. A **niche** is the position occupied by an organism and the role it plays within its community. ☐

Summary notes

Biomes

Biomes are the various regions of our planet that have a distinct climate and have a certain distinctive group of plants (flora) and animals (fauna) living there. Each biome is made up of a group of ecosystems. The distribution of biomes on the earth can be influenced by climate, for example temperature and rainfall.

Biomes on land include forests, grasslands and tundra (Figure 3.1). Water biomes include oceans, freshwater lochs and shallow, salt-water seas.

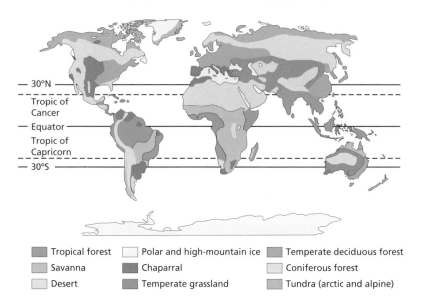

■ Tropical forest	□ Polar and high-mountain ice	■ Temperate deciduous forest
■ Savanna	■ Chaparral	■ Coniferous forest
□ Desert	■ Temperate grassland	■ Tundra (arctic and alpine)

Figure 3.1 Some global biomes

Components of an ecosystem

An ecosystem is a natural biological unit in which organisms interact with their environment. The components that make up the ecosystem are the **habitat**, **populations** and **communities**.

A habitat is the place where an organism lives, such as a pond, a rock pool, soil or leaf litter. A population is the total number of organisms of the same species that live in a particular habitat, such as the number of red deer on a piece of moorland. The community is the name given to all the different populations of organisms living in a habitat. A rock-pool community might be made up of the populations of seaweed, crabs, shrimps, small fish and sea anemones.

Ecological niche

The niche of an organism is the role that it plays. It refers to its whole way of life and includes its interactions with other organisms in the community and the resources it takes from its habitat. The table below describes some of the niche components for heather plants on Scottish moorland.

Niche component	Brief niche description for heather plants
Habitat	Moorland on acidic soil
Feeding level	Producer; photosynthetic green plant
Mode of life	Rooted in moorland soil; provides food and shelter for moorland animal community
Use of resources	Survives in soil in which water and nutrients are scarce

Biodiversity

Biodiversity is the term used to describe the variety and relative abundance of species present in an ecosystem.

Factors affecting the biodiversity in an ecosystem

Biodiversity is affected by the following factors.

- abiotic factors
- biotic factors
- human influences, which can be abiotic or biotic

Abiotic factors are non-living or physical factors that affect organisms and include light, moisture, temperature, pH, wind speed and oxygen availability.

Biotic factors are related directly to living organisms and include factors such as grazing, competition for food and space, predation and disease.

Human activities affect biodiversity because they influence both abiotic factors, such as pH and temperature, and biotic factors, including grazing and predation, which affect the organisms within an ecosystem. Some human influences are shown in the table below and some are discussed in Key Area 3.5.

> **Hints & tips** ⭐
>
> Remember, sometimes humans can improve biodiversity by their activities.

Human activity	Example	Effect on biodiversity
Habitat destruction	Clear-felling of tropical rainforest	Total removal of biodiversity from an area, leading to climate change
	Overgrazing of natural dry grassland by cattle	Loss of biodiversity, leading to soil erosion and desertification
Pollution	Burning of fossil fuels, polluting the atmosphere	Loss of lichens and other plants, which then affects food chains
	Discharging untreated sewage into waterways	De-oxygenation of water and collapse of food chains
Hunting and fishing	Overhunting of game animals	Extinction of key species and wider effects on many food chains
	Overfishing for white fish	Loss of fish stocks and collapse of marine food chains
Conservation	Setting up wildlife reserves	Protects habitats and wild populations, restoring biodiversity
	Captive breeding of endangered species	Increases wild populations through release schemes

Types of overgrazing and their effects

Overgrazing of livestock on natural grasslands: cattle in the USA

In many parts of the world, including the southern USA in the middle of the twentieth century, humans have tried to increase the numbers of cattle grazing on natural dry grasslands. The increased pressure of grazing made it impossible for grasses to regenerate green parts and resulted in loss of plants. This meant that there were no longer as many grass roots holding soils in place and, during dry periods, soil was eroded by wind. Loss of the soil resulted in desertification. ⇨

⇨

Overgrazing by wild animals whose numbers are too high: red deer in Scotland

Humans have removed the natural predators of red deer in Scotland and promoted high deer populations to suit the needs of deer hunting. The deer overgraze their environment, especially favouring tree seedlings. This has led to the increased failure of the native forests to regenerate and a reduction in the numbers of species such as rowan. In turn, loss of forest reduces overall biodiversity.

Key words

Abiotic – refers to physical factors, such as temperature and light intensity, that affect ecosystems

Biodiversity – refers to the number and abundance of species

Biome – region of the planet with characteristic climate, flora and fauna

Biotic – factor related to the biological aspects of an ecosystem such as predation and competition

Community – all the organisms living in a habitat

Ecosystem – natural biological unit composed of habitats, populations and communities

Fauna – the animals of a particular region

Flora – the plants of a particular region

Grazing – method of feeding on plants by herbivores

Habitat the place where an organism lives

Habitat destruction – human destruction of natural habitat by activities such as deforestation and over-grazing livestock on natural grassland

Niche – the role an organism has within its community in an ecosystem

Over-exploitation – human activities, such as overfishing, overhunting and overgrazing, that cause extinctions and destroy the food web balance

Pollution – environmental damage caused by humans usually by release of substances to the environment

Precipitation – water such as rain, snow, sleet, hail, dew

Predation – obtaining food by hunting and killing prey organisms

Questions ?

A Restricted-response questions (1 mark each)

1 Give the definition of a biome.
2 Give **three** examples of global biomes.
3 Give **two** factors that affect the global distribution of biomes.
4 State what is meant by the following terms.
  a) ecosystem
  b) biodiversity
5 Give **two** examples of abiotic factors in an ecosystem.
6 Give **two** examples of biotic factors in an ecosystem.
7 State what is meant by an organism's niche.

⇨

⇨
B Extended-response questions (2 or 3 marks)

1 Give **one** example of human influences that might affect biodiversity in an ecosystem and describe its effect. (2)
2 Describe what is meant by the following terms:
   a) competition
   b) predation (2)
3 Explain how each of the following factors can affect organisms in an ecosystem.
   a) light
   b) temperature
   c) nutrient availability (3)
4 Give an account of the factors that define an organism's niche. (3)

Key Area 3.2
Energy in ecosystems

Key points ❗

1 At each level in a food chain 90% of the energy that entered that level is not available to pass to the next level. ☐

2 The energy that is lost at each level of a food chain is mainly lost as heat and movement. ☐

3 At each level of a food chain, some energy remains stored in undigested material. ☐

4 A **pyramid of numbers** is a diagram that represents the relative numbers of organisms at each stage of a food chain. ☐

5 A **pyramid of biomass** is a diagram that shows the relative total masses of organisms at each level of a food chain. ☐

6 A **pyramid of energy** is a diagram that shows the relative total energy in the bodies of all organisms at each level of a food chain. ☐

7 Pyramids of biomass and energy are usually similar in shape with a broad base representing producers, reducing to a narrow apex representing carnivores. ☐

8 Pyramids of number often have a similar shape to pyramids of energy and biomass but there can be differences depending on the individual sizes of the organisms involved in the food chain. ☐

9 Nitrogen is cycled in ecosystems. ☐

10 The **nitrogen cycle** is dependent on various species of bacteria. ☐

11 **Decomposers** are organisms that help to convert proteins in dead organisms and the nitrogenous waste from living organisms to **ammonium** compounds. ☐

12 **Nitrifying bacteria** convert ammonium into nitrates, which can be taken up by plants. ☐

13 **Denitrifying bacteria** convert nitrates into nitrogen gas, which is released to the atmosphere. ☐

14 **Nitrogen-fixing bacteria** convert nitrogen gas to nitrates. ☐

15 Some species of nitrogen-fixing bacteria live free in soils and some species live in **root nodules** of certain plants. ☐

16 Plant and animal proteins are made up from amino acid units, which are produced using nitrogen from nitrates. ☐

17 **Competition** can occur if organisms struggle for the same resources that are in short supply. ☐

18 **Interspecific competition** occurs if organisms of different species compete. ☐

19 **Intraspecific competition** refers to competition between organisms of the same species. ☐

Summary notes

Energy flow in an ecosystem

The sun is the ultimate source of energy for an ecosystem. Light energy from the sun is trapped by green plants and converted to the chemical energy that maintains all life on Earth.

Green plants are called **producers** because they can produce their own food by the process of photosynthesis. **Consumers** obtain energy by eating other organisms. Those which eat plants only are **herbivores**. Those which eat animals only are **carnivores**. **Omnivores** eat both animals and plants. The flow or transfer of energy through different feeding levels in an ecosystem can be shown by the use of food chain diagrams.

Food chains

A food chain is a diagram that shows the feeding relationships of organisms living together in a particular ecosystem (Figure 3.2). A food chain always starts with a green plant, the producer. Various consumer levels are shown connected by arrows, which indicate the direction of energy flow. Waste materials from organisms and the remains of dead organisms are passed into decomposer food chains.

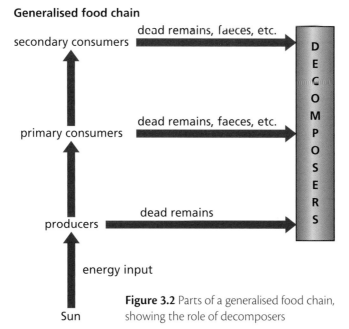

Figure 3.2 Parts of a generalised food chain, showing the role of decomposers

An example of a simple food chain from a Scottish moorland is shown in Figure 3.3.

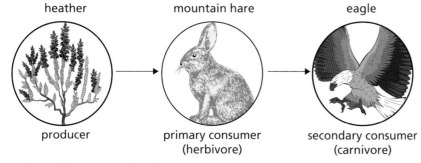

Figure 3.3 Scottish moorland food chain

Energy transfer in food chains

The energy in the food that is eaten by a consumer is used in a number of ways.

Growth

Some energy is used to build new body tissue. This energy is trapped in body tissues and is available to be passed on to the next level in the chain.

Heat and movement

A lot of the energy is used to maintain body temperature and more is used in moving around. All of this can be lost as heat. This energy is not available to the next level in the chain.

Undigested material and uneaten remains

Undigested waste material and uneaten remains contain chemical energy. This energy is lost from the food chain. However, the energy contained in the undigested waste or uneaten remains is available to decomposers such as bacteria and fungi.

About 90% of the energy that enters a food chain level is ultimately lost and so only 10% is available to be passed on to the next level in the chain. This general pattern is shown in Figure 3.4.

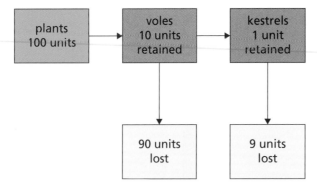

Figure 3.4 Units of energy flow and loss in a food chain

Decomposers

Decomposers are a group of organisms that obtain their energy by breaking down undigested waste, uneaten remains and dead bodies. Bacteria and fungi are examples of decomposers. Decomposers release and recycle nutrients, which can then be taken up and used by plants.

Pyramid diagrams

Pyramids of numbers

A pyramid of numbers is a diagram that shows the total number of organisms at each stage in a food chain (Figure 3.5).

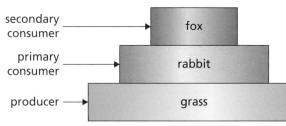

Figure 3.5 Typical pyramid of numbers

Moving up the pyramid, the number of organisms decreases but the size of each individual usually increases. The energy lost at each stage in the food chain limits the numbers of organisms that can survive at the next level. Pyramids of numbers do not always result in a true pyramid shape. Figure 3.6 shows two examples of this.

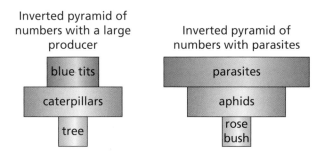

Figure 3.6 Two unusual pyramids of numbers

Pyramids of biomass

The pyramid of biomass is a diagram that shows the total mass of all the organisms at each stage in a food chain (Figure 3.7).

Figure 3.7 Pyramid of biomass

Pyramids of biomass are usually pyramid shaped because each level gains all its mass from the level below and so it cannot have more mass than that level. In other words an animal cannot weigh more than it eats! Figure 3.8 shows how one of the unusual pyramids of number shown above produces a true pyramid of biomass.

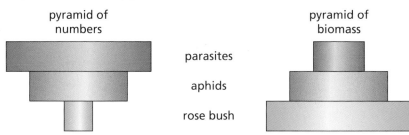

Figure 3.8 Pyramid of numbers with its pyramid of biomass

The biomass at each level is dependent on the energy passed on at each stage in the food chain and can vary throughout the year.

Pyramid of energy

This is a diagram that shows the energy available at each stage in a food chain (Figure 3.9).

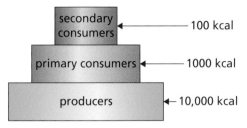

Figure 3.9 Pyramid of energy

A pyramid of energy is the most realistic way of representing energy levels in a food chain and always has the shape of a true pyramid.

The nitrogen cycle

Nitrogen is a chemical element necessary for protein and nucleic acid formation. Plants make the protein they need using nitrate absorbed from the soil. Animals eat plants and convert plant protein into animal protein. There is more about nucleic acid and protein in Key Areas 1.4 and 1.5.

Nitrification

Decomposers such as bacteria and fungi break down both the protein in dead organisms and their nitrogenous waste products and convert them to ammonium compounds. Nitrifying bacteria in the soil convert the ammonium compounds into nitrites and then into nitrates. The process of converting other compounds into nitrates is called nitrification.

Nitrogen fixation

Legumes are a group of plants, including peas, beans and clover, that contain nitrogen-fixing bacteria in small swellings in their roots called root nodules. Nitrogen-fixing bacteria are also found living free in the soil. These bacteria convert nitrogen gas from the air into nitrates. This process is called nitrogen fixation.

Lightning is a natural event, which converts atmospheric nitrogen to nitrate. This nitrate is then dissolved in rain, falls to the ground and enters the soil.

Denitrification

Denitrifying bacteria, especially in waterlogged soil, carry out a process called denitrification that results in the conversion of nitrates into nitrogen gas, which is released into the air, completing the cycle (Figure 3.10).

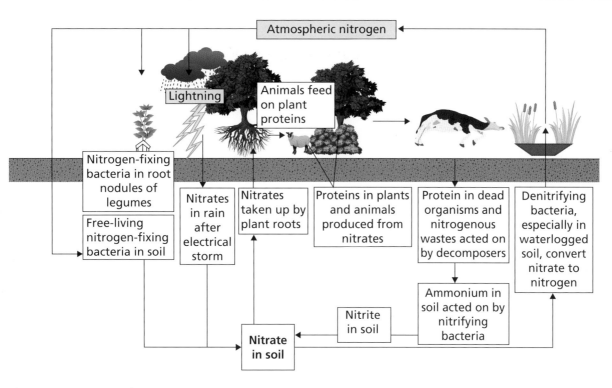

Figure 3.10 Nitrogen cycle in an ecosystem

Key words

Ammonium – NH_4; a nitrogen-containing waste product of decomposition

Carnivore – consumer which eats other animals

Competition – interaction between organisms seeking the same limited resources

Consumer – animal which eats ready-made foods

Decomposers – organisms such as bacteria and fungi responsible for the breakdown of dead organic material

Denitrifying bacteria – convert nitrates in the soil into nitrogen gas, which is released into the atmosphere

Herbivore – consumer which eats plants

Interspecific competition – competition between organisms of two different species for a common resource

Intraspecific competition – competition between organisms within the same species

Nitrifying bacteria – produce nitrate, which is released into soil

Nitrogen cycle – sequence of events or processes involved in the recycling of nitrogen

Nitrogen-fixing bacteria – bacteria found free living in the soil or in the root nodules of some plants that convert nitrogen gas into nitrate

Omnivore – consumer which eats a mixture of plants and animals

Producer – organism that synthesises its own food

Pyramid of biomass – diagram that shows the relative total masses of the organisms at each level in a food chain.

Pyramid of energy – diagram that shows the relative quantities of energy at each level in a food chain

Pyramid of numbers – diagram that shows the relative numbers of organisms at each level in a food chain

Root nodule – small swelling on the roots of plants such as peas, beans and clover that contains nitrogen-fixing bacteria

Questions ?

A Restricted-response questions (1 mark each)

1 Draw a food chain diagram for grass plants that are grazed by rabbits, which are preyed upon by foxes.
2 The diagram shows a simple food chain for an oak wood.
   oak leaf → caterpillar → blue tit → sparrowhawk
   Name the following from the food chain:
   a) a producer
   b) a primary consumer
   c) a carnivore
3 Account for the loss of energy at each level in a food chain.
4 State why nitrates are needed by living organisms.
5 Give the difference between interspecific and intraspecific competition.

B Extended-response questions (2 or 3 marks)

1 Give the meanings of the following terms:
   a) habitat   c) community
   b) population   d) ecosystem   (2)
2 Explain why decomposition can account for some of the losses that occur to energy transfer
   in a food chain.   (2)
3 Pyramid diagrams are used to represent food chains. Explain what is represented by the following
   pyramids:
   a) numbers
   b) biomass
   c) energy   (3)
4 State the meaning of the following processes of the nitrogen cycle:
   a) nitrogen fixation   c) nitrification
   b) denitrification   d) decomposition   (3)
5 Give an account of the roles of bacteria in the nitrogen cycle.   (3)

Key Area 3.3

Sampling techniques and measurement of abiotic and biotic factors

Key points !

1 Abiotic factors are physical factors such as light intensity, temperature, pH and moisture. ☐
2 Abiotic factors can be measured using instruments designed to give numerical values. ☐
3 Biotic factors are biological factors such as predation, grazing and competition between organisms. ☐
4 A **sample** can be taken to represent a population of an organism in a habitat or an ecosystem. ☐
5 **Quadrats** can be used to sample organisms that are fixed, or partly fixed, to a surface or those that spend a significant time motionless. ☐
6 **Pitfall traps** can be used to sample invertebrate animals that move around on surfaces. ☐
7 Quadrats and pitfall traps can be used **quantitatively** or **qualitatively** to estimate populations of organisms. ☐
8 Sampling techniques such as those involving quadrats or pitfall traps are limited in what they can measure and can potentially create **sources of error**. ☐

Summary notes

Abiotic factors

Abiotic factors are non-living or physical factors that affect organisms, such as light, moisture, temperature, pH, wind speed and oxygen availability.

Biotic factors

Biotic factors are related directly to living organisms and include grazing, competition for food and space, predation and disease.

Sampling organisms in an ecosystem

It is usually impossible to count all the plants and animals living in an ecosystem so biologists use various methods for estimating the types and numbers of organisms present.

A **sample** can be taken to represent a population of organisms in an ecosystem. To be representative, appropriate numbers of samples are required.

Techniques used for sampling organisms

Quadrats are used to sample low growing plants and very slow moving animals. A quadrat marks off an exact area of ground so that the organisms in that area can be identified and counted (Figure 3.11). Quadrats are often placed randomly in an area to improve reliability.

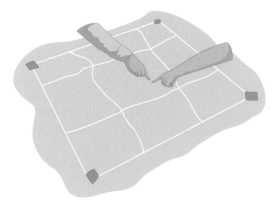

Figure 3.11 Quadrat in use

Pitfall traps can be used to sample small invertebrate animals living on the soil surface or in leaf litter (Figure 3.12). Animals fall into the trap and are unable to climb out again. The traps are usually set in a random way. It is essential to check traps regularly since predation and scavenging can occur within traps if left too long.

Stones to prevent rain flooding the trap or birds or other predators from removing the trapped animals

Jar or pot sunk in a hole in the ground

Figure 3.12 Pitfall trap in use

Qualitative results

Very often, quadrats and pitfall traps are used to give qualitative results. They simply show if a species is present or absent in the sampling area.

Quantitative results

Quadrats and pitfall traps can be used to estimate populations of organisms quantitatively. This means that the results can be converted into actual figures.

It is possible to exactly count plants within a known size of quadrat, average this result for several quadrats and then express the result as number of plants per square metre. For example, in an investigation, five 1 × 1 metre quadrats were used to estimate the daisy population of an area of parkland grass. The results are shown in the table on page 111.

Quadrat	Daisy plants (per square metre)
1	6
2	3
3	12
4	8
5	6
Average	**7 daisy plants per square metre**

Invertebrates such as ground beetles can be caught in pitfall traps, marked with a speck of paint and then released. Resetting the traps and recapturing some of the original animals allows us to calculate an estimate of population density. For example, in an investigation, five traps were set overnight in ploughed soil in a 100 m² cereal field. 40 beetles were captured, marked and released. The following night the trapping was repeated and 3 of the original marked animals were recaptured out of a total catch of 12. The population density is estimated as follows:

$$\text{population of beetles} = \frac{\text{number of beetles marked and released} \times \text{number in second sample}}{\text{number of marked beetles in second sample}}$$

$$= \frac{40 \times 12}{3} = 160$$

$$\text{population of beetles} = 160 \text{ beetles per } 100 \text{ m}^2$$

Possible limitations and sources of error in using sampling techniques

It is important that investigators plan their sampling, choosing the best sampling technique and the optimum number of samples for their purposes. The main sources of error usually lie with poor selection of technique or numbers of samples taken and with human error in carrying out the technique.

In general, large numbers of random samples should be taken and extreme care used when carrying out the sampling and identifying organisms present in the samples. Results should always be treated carefully and their reliability taken into account. The table below shows some limitations and sources of error in using quadrat and pitfall trap sampling.

Technique	Limitations	Possible errors
Quadrat sampling	Generally only suitable for low-growing, rooted plants	Quadrats may not be placed randomly or according to the planned method Inappropriate size of quadrat selected
	Quadrat size	Too few quadrats used
	Reliability limited by number of samples possible	Plants misidentified or overlooked
Pitfall trap sampling	Generally only suitable for small, surface-crawling invertebrates	Traps may not be placed randomly or according to the planned method Inappropriate size of trap selected
	Pitfall trap size	Too few traps used
	Reliability limited by number of traps set	Traps badly set or not emptied on time; invertebrates misidentified or lost from sample

Hints & tips

Remember: Repeat, Random, Reliable and Representative

Measuring abiotic factors

An abiotic factor is a non-living factor often related to climate that can affect the distribution of organisms in an ecosystem. There is a range of modern instruments that can be used to measure these factors. Most have a probe to contact the environment and an easily read scale to show the result.

The table below shows some abiotic factors and methods used to measure them.

Abiotic factor	Measuring instrument
Soil pH	Soil pH meter
Light intensity	Light meter
Temperature	Thermometer
Moisture level	Moisture meter
Oxygen concentration	Oxygen meter

Figure 3.13 shows the type of meter that is commonly available in garden centres and used by gardeners to obtain information on abiotic factors related to growing plants.

Figure 3.13 An example of a meter used to measure abiotic factors

Notice the probe, which has to be cleaned and dried between readings, and the value recorded on the scale, which is easily read. It is good practice to average a large number of readings to help minimise error and increase reliability.

Sources of error

As in sampling, errors can creep into the measurement of abiotic factors. The techniques need to be applied with care, for example remembering to clean and dry probes between samples and to read scales accurately. Appropriately large numbers of readings are required for reliable averages to be calculated.

Hints & tips

Remember: **ROAR =** *Repeat, Obtain an Average to increase Reliability*

Key words

Pitfall trap – sampling technique used to trap animals living on the soil surface or in leaf litter
Quadrat – square frame of known area used for sampling the abundance and distribution of slow or non-moving organisms
Qualitative – able to be expressed as presence or absence; referring to results from sampling
Quantitative – able to be expressed using numerical values; referring to results from sampling
Sample – a representative part of a larger quantity
Source of error – the origin of a mistake in drawing conclusions from experiments

Questions ?

A Restricted-response questions (1 mark each)

1 Give **two** examples of abiotic factors.
2 Describe the following biotic factors:
   a) predation
   b) competition
3 State what is meant by a sample.
4 Name techniques that could be used to sample the following organisms:
   a) dandelions rooted in a field of rye grass
   b) beetles that move around the soil surface at night in grassy areas
5 Give **two** sources of error that can affect sampling using quadrats.
6 Give **two** sources of error that can affect sampling using pitfall traps.

B Extended-response questions (2 or 3 marks)

1 Explain how a named abiotic factor can affect the distribution of a green plant. (2)
2 Explain how a named abiotic factor can affect the distribution of an animal. (2)
3 Explain what is meant by qualitative and quantitative sampling. (2)
4 Describe how you might estimate the number of dandelion plants per square metre in a large grassy park with an area of 100 m². (3)
5 Describe how you might estimate the population of ground beetles living in a small lawn with an area of 10 m². (3)

Key Area 3.4
Adaptation, natural selection and the evolution of species

Key points ⚠

1 A **species** is a group of organisms that freely interbreed to produce fertile offspring. ☐
2 **Mutations** are random, spontaneous changes in genetic material and the only source of new alleles. ☐
3 Rates of mutation can be increased by environmental factors such as certain types of **radiation** and chemicals. ☐
4 Mutations can be neutral and have little effect on the organism with the mutation. ☐
5 Mutations can be harmful if they give the organism a disadvantage and so decrease its chances of survival. ☐
6 Mutations can be beneficial if they give the organism an advantage and so increase its chances of survival. ☐
7 Living organisms can evolve and adapt to changing environmental conditions. ☐
8 Variation exists within populations of living organisms. ☐
9 Living organisms often produce more offspring than the environment can support. ☐
10 Natural selection acts on variation in populations in such a way that only those with the best **adaptations** survive to reproduce. ☐
11 An adaptation is a feature of an organism that helps it to survive. ☐
12 The intensity of a selective factor such as predation is called **selection pressure**. ☐
13 The best-adapted organisms with favourable characteristics have a **selective advantage**. ☐
14 Individuals with a selective advantage survive to pass on their beneficial characteristics to offspring. ☐
15 **Speciation** is the evolution of two or more species from one original ancestor species. ☐
16 Speciation can occur when natural selection acts on an isolated population, causing it to evolve into a new species. ☐

Summary notes

Evolution

In the nineteenth century, Charles Darwin used the idea of natural selection to explain the process of evolution that has resulted in the variety of living organisms we see on Earth today.

Species

A species is a group of organisms that are so similar to one another that they can freely interbreed and produce fertile offspring. All species that exist today have come about by the process of evolution.

Variation

As you saw in Key Area 2.5, members of a species are varied and much of their variation is passed onto their offspring. The only way in which new variation can appear is when errors in genetic material arise through a process called mutation.

Mutation

Mutations are spontaneous, random events that cause changes to the genetic information of an organism. They can affect single genes or whole chromosomes. Mutation is the only source of new alleles in a population. Mutations occur at a very low frequency, but environmental factors, such as radiation and some chemicals, can increase the rate of mutation.

Mutations can be neutral and have little effect on an organism. Mutations can be harmful and give the organism a disadvantage and so decrease its chance of survival. Alternatively mutations can confer an advantage to an organism and increase its chances of survival.

> **Hints & tips** ⭐
>
> Remember: ROLF =
> Mutations are of Random
> Occurrence and Low
> Frequency.

Natural selection

Organisms produce more offspring than the environment can support due to the limited resources available. Members of a species show variation in their characteristics through the different mutations they carry. A struggle for survival follows as offspring compete for limited resources such as space, food and light.

Natural selection results in the survival of those organisms whose variation makes them best suited to their environment. Some individuals survive and others do not – this is survival of the fittest. Selection pressure is a factor that acts on members of a population and results in the death of some members of the population and the survival of others. Examples of selection pressures include predation, disease and various aspects of the climate such as rainfall and temperature.

Speciation

Speciation is the term used to describe the formation of two or more species from one original species. The process happens in a series of stages:

1 **Isolation:** populations of a species can become isolated or separated from each other. Isolating mechanisms such as tracts of water or mountain chains are barriers to gene exchange or gene flow between the sub-populations of a species. Separation prevents the sub-populations from interbreeding.

2 **Mutation:** different mutations are likely to arise in the different sub-populations. Beneficial mutations occurring in one sub-population will allow the mutants to survive, reproduce and pass on their beneficial alleles to their offspring.

3 **Natural selection:** the environment of each sub-population is different, as are the selection pressures. Natural selection of the best-suited individuals in each sub-population is therefore different. Those with favourable characteristics have an advantage over others. They survive, reproduce and pass on these favourable characteristics to their offspring. In this way the sub-populations gradually evolve along different paths.

4 **Speciation:** after a very long period of time, the isolated sub-populations change so much genetically that they can no longer interbreed to produce fertile offspring even if they are able to reach each other. This shows that they are completely new species. Speciation has occurred.

Speciation in action: Darwin's finches

The Galapagos Islands are isolated in the Pacific Ocean 600 kilometres from the South American coast. It is thought that a species of finch-like bird arrived on these islands hundreds of thousands of years ago after being forced to leave the mainland, probably due to overcrowding there. The birds spread out over the islands and lack of competition allowed their populations to rise.

Groups became isolated on the individual islands because it was dangerous to cross the windy and choppy seas. Different mutations occurred within the populations of different islands and natural selection varied between the islands because of habitat differences. Over thousands of generations, differences between populations built up and today there are about 13 new species of Darwin's finches. The finch species differ strikingly in terms of beak shapes and sizes, allowing them to exploit particular foods available in their habitat, as shown in Figure 3.14.

insect-eating 'warbler' finch (tree dweller)

insect-eating 'woodpecker' finch (tree dweller)

fruit-eating finch (tree dweller)

seed-eating finch (ground dweller)

cactus-eating finch (ground dweller)

Figure 3.14 Darwin's finches

Adaptation

The beak shapes of Darwin's finches are adaptations for survival. It is a characteristic of evolution that adaptations emerge in different species. The table below shows some adaptations in mammals and how they help survival.

Species	Adaptations
Camel	Long eyelashes and ears covered with hairs to keep wind-blown sand out of its eyes and ear canals; wide foot pads to spread weight and avoid sinking into sand
Arctic fox	Changes coat colour from brown in summer to white in winter for camouflage when stalking prey; small ears prevent excessive heat loss in cold conditions
Desert rat	Does not sweat so that it can conserve water; is nocturnal to avoid hot conditions, which could cause overheating; burrows into lower layers of moist sand for protection during the day

Sometimes natural selection produces adaptations in which pairs of organisms seem to have evolved together. Some examples are given in the table below.

Organism pair	Description of partnership
Acacia tree and acacia ants	Acacia ants live inside the hollowed-out thorns of acacia trees and feed from special liquid foods supplied by the tree. In return the ants provide protection from other animals that seek to eat the acacia leaves
Darwin's orchid and hawkmoth pollinators	Darwin's orchid has nectar produced at the base of flower tubes that can be as long as 25 cm. It has a hawkmoth pollinator with a tongue long enough to reach the nectar. The moth seeks out the orchid because it is the only species that can reach the nectar, so eliminating competition. As the moth feeds on the nectar it pollinates the orchid

Key words

Adaptation – feature of an organism that helps it to survive

Mutation – a random and spontaneous change in the structure of a gene, chromosome or number of chromosomes; only source of new alleles

Radiation – energy in wave form such as light, sound, heat, X-rays, gamma rays

Selection pressure – factor such as predation or disease that affects a population, resulting in the death of some individuals and survival of others

Selective advantage – an increased chance of survival for an organism because of possession of favourable characteristics

Speciation – formation of two or more species from an original ancestral species

Species – organisms with similar characteristics and with the ability to interbreed to produce fertile offspring

Questions ?

A Restricted-response questions (1 mark each)

1 Give a definition of the term species.
2 State what is meant by genetic mutation.
3 Name **two** factors that can increase the rate of mutation.
4 State what is meant by a neutral mutation.
5 State what is meant by the term natural selection.
6 Give the meaning of the term adaptation.
7 Give an example of an adaptation in a named animal.

B Extended-response questions (2 or 3 marks)

1 Explain the importance of mutations in the evolution of new species. (2)
2 Explain what is meant by the terms selection pressure and selective advantage. (2)
3 Give an account of speciation. (3)

Key Area 3.5
Human impact on the environment

Key points !

1 The increasing human population requires an increased food supply. ☐
2 Methods of increasing food supply have included the use of **fertilisers, pesticides, biological control** and **genetically modified (GM) crops.** ☐
3 Fertilisers can leach from fields into freshwater, increasing the effects of **algal blooms.** ☐
4 When algal blooms die, they are decomposed by **aerobic** bacteria, which multiply and reduce the oxygen concentration in the water. ☐
5 Pesticides can accumulate in the bodies of organisms and so build up along food chains. ☐
6 **Toxicity** levels of pesticides in the bodies of carnivores can build up to the extent that the animal or its reproduction is damaged. ☐
7 The presence, abundance or absence of **indicator species** can reveal information about the environment and level of pollution present. ☐
8 Biological control relies on natural solutions to pest problems, such as making use of natural predators or parasites. ☐
9 Crop species can be genetically modified to increase their yields without the need for fertilisers or pesticides. ☐
10 Biological control and GM crops are alternatives to intensive farming methods. ☐
11 Using biological control and GM crops rather than intensive farming methods could result in less damage to the environment. ☐

Summary notes
Human population

The human population is continuing to increase, as shown in Figure 3.15. The milestones show the dates at which the population had added a further billion. Some cultural changes that contributed to population rise are also shown.

To provide enough food to meet the needs of a rising population, methods of increasing food yield are needed. Farming is the main way in which humans guarantee food, and much effort has gone into increasing yields from farms. Some methods of increasing food production have had negative effects on biodiversity, as discussed in Key Area 3.1.

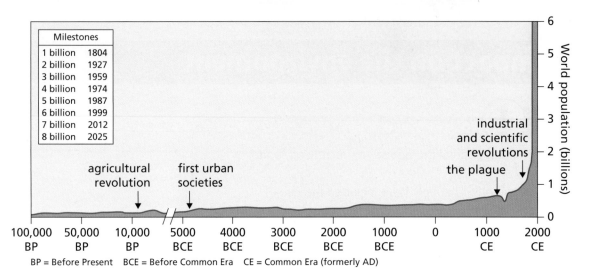

Milestones	
1 billion	1804
2 billion	1927
3 billion	1959
4 billion	1974
5 billion	1987
6 billion	1999
7 billion	2012
8 billion	2025

BP = Before Present   BCE = Before Common Era   CE = Common Era (formerly AD)

Figure 3.15 Human population growth, with milestones

Intensive farming

Intensive farming usually involves growing single crop species, such as wheat, in enormous fields. This allows efficient planting, crop treatments and harvesting. It is associated with heavy use of fertilisers and pesticides.

Fertilisers and pesticides

Fertilisers are often used to enhance the minerals in soil and improve the growth of the crop, so increasing yield. Various pesticides can be applied to the crop to kill a range of pests and so increase the amount of crop available to be harvested.

Problems in the use of fertilisers

Fertilisers can leach from the fields into the freshwater of rivers, lochs and ponds. This can happen when heavy rainfall washes fertiliser from fields into waterways. The fertiliser greatly increases the growth of algae in the water and increases the effects of algal blooms on the freshwater ecosystem. An algal bloom is an abundance of algal cells, which can block out light to lower levels of a body of water and cause the death of other water plants.

In autumn, nutrients run out and there is less light for photosynthesis. The algae in the bloom start to die and their bodies are decomposed by aerobic bacteria. The bacteria increase in number and so reduce the oxygen concentration in the water. The decrease in oxygen concentration results in the death of many other organisms.

Problems in the use of pesticides

Pesticides are chemicals that are sprayed onto crops to kill pests. Insecticides kill insects, such as greenfly, that feed on plants and reduce crop yield. Some insecticides are not specific and kill other insects as well as the target pest. This then affects other organisms that feed on the insects and therefore affects other food chains. Some pesticides are persistent and can build up, accumulating in the bodies of organisms higher up the food chain. The toxicity levels of pesticide in the bodies of

Hints & tips

Fertilisers Feed crops

120

carnivores can build up to concentrations that can eventually cause harm to the organisms or damage their reproduction, as shown in Figure 3.16.

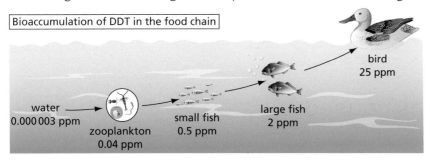

Bioaccumulation of DDT in the food chain

water 0.000 003 ppm
zooplankton 0.04 ppm
small fish 0.5 ppm
large fish 2 ppm
bird 25 ppm

Figure 3.16 Accumulation of the persistent insecticide DDT along a food chain

The story of DDT

One of the most well-known insecticides is DDT, which was used very successfully from the 1940s and was responsible for controlling populations of some species of mosquito in certain areas of southern Europe, where these insects were involved in the spread of malaria.

This undoubtedly saved millions of human lives. However, DDT is non-selective and persistent, so it killed insects other than mosquitoes and accumulated in the food chain. Every molecule of DDT ever used is still somewhere in the world's ecosystems! One consequence of the use of this insecticide was very severe damage to populations of predatory birds and some species were brought near to extinction. As new insecticides became available, DDT was banned in many developed countries in the 1970s. Predatory bird populations have since recovered.

Do you believe that DDT should be banned in countries where it could still be needed as a cheap insecticide to limit the spread of malaria?

Biological control

Biological control involves using organisms such as natural predators or parasites to control pest numbers. This can work well in enclosed situations such as glasshouses but is more difficult in open fields.

Biological pest control works particularly well when the pest has been introduced to the ecosystem and has no natural predators. An example is the cotton cushion scale insect, which was accidentally introduced to California from Australia in the late nineteenth century. In California it multiplied out of control and destroyed large numbers of citrus trees, a major Californian crop. So a ladybird beetle, one of the scale insect's natural predators, was also introduced from Australia, and quickly reduced the numbers of scale insects to a safe level. Today both species coexist in California, but at low population densities.

The control species have to be chosen carefully to ensure that they can survive in their new environment and attack the pest only, not other native species. It is vital that they do not carry disease into the new ecosystem and that they will not become a pest due to lack of predators or parasites controlling their numbers.

Control species should be trialled in a controlled area, such as a greenhouse, before being released into the wild. If proper precautions are not taken, biological control can lead to ecological disaster.

Ecological problems caused by biological control

Cane toads were introduced to Australia from Hawaii in 1935 to control beetles that feed on sugar cane crops. The cane toads were poisonous to predators and ate a variety of prey, including native marsupials. They are still spreading through Australia and are now more of a problem to biodiversity than the original beetles.

Guppies have been introduced to many parts of the world in the hope that they might control mosquitoes by eating their larvae, and so reduce the incidence of malaria. Although this has worked to some extent, the guppies usually have a negative effect on the native fish species by out-competing them.

Do you think that biological control methods are worth risking?

Integrated pest management (IPM)

Some farmers use integrated pest management, which involves using a combination of biological control and pesticides to control crop pests. This method can help to reduce the amount of pesticide that farmers need to use.

Genetically modified (GM) crops

Genetically modified or genetically engineered refers to organisms whose genetic information has been altered, usually by the addition of a useful gene from another organism. Common GM foods include tomatoes, maize, rice, cabbage, potato and soyabean. There is more about GM organisms in Key Area 1.6, page 24.

Crop plants can be genetically modified to increase their yields and also to reduce the need to use fertilisers or pesticides. Genetically modified herbicide-resistant crops can be sprayed with herbicide to kill weeds and so reduce competition for water and minerals. In the USA, the genetic modification providing herbicide resistance in crop plants has been found to have been passed on to some naturally occurring weeds. Other examples of GM crops include the following:

- A variety of cauliflower has been genetically modified by inserting scorpion genes. These produce a poison that acts as an insecticide and kills the caterpillars that are pests of the cauliflower crop.
- GM rice (golden rice) has been developed to contain the substance beta-carotene, which enables children to produce vitamin A. This can prevent a form of blindness caused by lack of vitamin A in the diet.

Alternatives to intensive farming

Biological control methods and the use of GM crops are alternatives to intensive farming methods that use large amounts of fertilisers and pesticides to increase crop yield. Using biological control and GM crops could reduce the use of these chemicals and result in less damage to the environment.

Biological indicators of pollution

Organisms that, by their presence, abundance or absence, show conditions in the environment are called biological indicators. Some can indicate the level of pollution present and are called biological indicators of pollution.

Freshwater invertebrates: water pollution

Certain invertebrates can be used to reveal information about the oxygen concentration in the freshwater environment. Rivers with water that is clean and well oxygenated will usually have a greater variety of different species than one that has a low oxygen concentration.

Mayfly nymphs and stonefly nymphs are examples of freshwater invertebrates whose presence indicates clean, well-oxygenated water conditions.

Rivers that have a low oxygen concentration have a small number of different species. Those organisms that can tolerate the low oxygen concentrations will increase in number. They have adaptations that allow them to survive in these low-oxygen conditions. Sludgeworms contain haemoglobin, which helps them to absorb the limited oxygen in the water. Where these species are abundant, a high level of pollution is indicated. Figure 3.17 shows some freshwater invertebrates and the conditions they indicate.

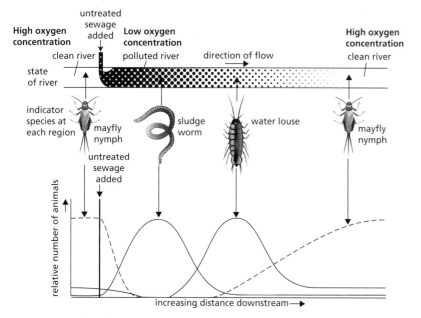

Figure 3.17 Effect of sewage on oxygen concentration and indictor organism populations in a river

Lichen: air pollution

Lichen is an organism that is used as a biological indicator of air pollution. Different species of lichen vary in their sensitivity to sulphur dioxide pollution produced by the burning of fossil fuels. Figure 3.18 shows the effect of sulphur dioxide pollution on the diversity of lichen species present in an ecosystem.

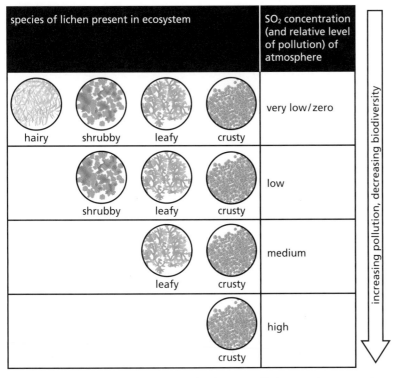

Figure 3.18 Effect of SO_2 pollution on the diversity of lichen species present in ecosystems

Key words

Aerobic – in the presence of, or involving the use of, oxygen
Algal bloom – a seasonal abundance of algae
Biological control – natural control of pests using natural predators, parasites etc.
Fertiliser – chemical added to the soil to improve plant growth or crop yield
Genetically modified (GM) – term given to a cell or organism that has had its genetic code altered, usually by adding a gene from another organism
Indicator species – organisms that by their presence, abundance or absence give information such as level of pollution in the environment
Pesticides – general name for chemicals used to kill organisms that damage or feed on crop plants
Toxicity – poison level

Questions ?

A Restricted-response questions (1 mark each)

1 State how each of the following improves crop yield in intensive farming methods:
   a) fertilisers
   b) pesticides
2 Give **one** benefit of intensive farming.
3 State what is meant by the term algal bloom.

4 Give the meaning of the term indicator species.

5 Give **one** example of an indicator species.

6 Name the gas that decreases in the water when aerobic bacteria decompose dead algae.

B Extended-response questions (2 or 3 marks)

1 Describe the link between farming methods and damage to the environment caused by use of fertilisers.

(3)

2 Describe the link between farming methods and damage to the environment caused by use of persistent pesticides.

(3)

3 Give the advantages of the following methods of increasing food supply:

a) GM crops

b) biological control of pests

(2)

Answers

Key Area 3.1

A Restricted-response questions (1 mark each)

1 a region of the planet with characteristic climate, fauna and flora

2 tropical rainforest, dry grassland, tundra, shallow seas…*(other possible answers)*   [any 3]

3 temperature, rainfall   [both]

4 a) habitat with its community and non-living components

b) variety and number of species   [both]

5 pH, temperature…*(other possible answers)*   [any 2]

6 grazing, predation…*(other possible answers)*   [any 2]

7 the role the organism plays within its community

B Extended-response questions (2 or 3 marks)

1 SO_2 pollution from burning fossil fuels, which damages plants; overgrazing, which damages plant communities and causes erosion of soil…*(other possible answers)*   [cause – 1, effect = 1]

2 a) struggle between or within species for resources that are in short supply

b) animals hunting and feeding on the flesh of other animals   [1 each = 2]

3 a) light affects the growth of green plants

b) temperature affects enzyme systems

c) nutrient availability affects plant growth   [1 each = 3]

4 what it feeds on; what feeds on it; what other resources it uses; what organisms it interacts with; what it adds to the environment   [any 3 = 3]

Answers

Key Area 3.2

A Restricted-response questions (1 mark each)

1 grass → rabbit → fox
2 a) oak leaf
   b) caterpillar
   c) blue tit or sparrowhawk   [all 3]
3 energy lost by movement and as heat   [both]
4 used to make proteins and nucleic acids   [both]
5 interspecific is competition between members of different species, intraspecific is between members of the same species   [both]

B Extended-response questions (2 or 3 marks)

1 a) place in which an organism lives
   b) number of a given species within a habitat
   c) all of the living organisms in a habitat
   d) a habitat with its community and non-living components   [all = 2, 3/2 = 1]

2 dead organisms from the chain entering the decomposition cycle; rather than being consumed by the next level of the food chain they enter the decomposer food chain   [1 each = 2]
3 a) populations of each organism at each level of a food chain
   b) total mass of organisms at each level of a food chain
   c) total energy available at each level of a food chain   [all 3 = 2, 2/1 = 1]
4 a) turning atmospheric nitrogen into nitrates by bacteria
   b) loss of nitrogen by conversion of nitrates into nitrogen gas
   c) production of nitrates from other compounds by soil bacteria
   d) breakdown of the bodies of organisms following death   [all 4 = 3, 3/2 = 2]
5 bacteria release nitrate from organic material in soil; convert atmospheric nitrogen to nitrates; convert soil nitrates to nitrogen gas; fix nitrogen directly inside certain plants   [any 3 = 3]

Answers

Key Area 3.3

A Restricted-response questions (1 mark each)

1 temperature, rainfall...(*other possible answers*)   [any 2]
2 a) predation is a relationship in which one animal hunts and eats another
   b) competition occurs when organisms struggle against others for similar resources   [both]
3 a small, representative portion of a larger quantity
4 a) quadrat
   b) pitfall trap   [both]
5 failure to use enough quadrats; using inappropriately sized quadrats; failure to randomise the quadrats   [any 2]

6 failure to use enough traps; inappropriately sized traps; failure to randomise distribution of traps; failure to check traps regularly   [any 2]

B Extended-response questions (2 or 3 marks)

1 light intensity – can affect photosynthesis; low rainfall – can cause loss of turgidity in cells and cause wilting in whole plants... (*other possible answers*)   [1 for factor + 1 for explanation]
2 temperature – can affect enzyme activity in animal cells; low rainfall – can lead to dehydration in animals...(*other possible answers*)   [1 for factor + 1 for explanation]

⇨

⇒
3 qualitative is simply recording species found; quantitative means counting individuals of each species present in a sample   [1 each = 2]
4 drop many 1 m² quadrats randomly across the area; count dandelion plants in each

quadrat; find the average number across all the quadrats used   [1 each = 3]
5 set a number of pitfall traps randomly across the lawn; count beetles in each trap; mark beetles; release and recapture; calculate estimated population   [all = 3, 4/3 = 2, 2/1 = 1]

Answers

Key Area 3.4

A Restricted-response questions (1 mark each)

1 group of organisms interbreeding to produce fertile young
2 random change in genetic material
3 radiation, chemicals
4 confers no advantage or disadvantage to the organism
5 survival of the fittest
6 special feature of an organism that gives it the ability to survive
7 camouflage in fish; insulation in whales; neck length in giraffe; coat colour in polar bears... *(other possible answers)*

B Extended-response questions (2 or 3 marks)

1 mutations increase variation; natural selection acts on variation to change species over time   [1 each = 2]
2 the strength of natural selection; the extent to which an adaptation allows survival   [1 each = 2]
3 members of a species isolated from each other; different mutations occur in different groups; natural selection acts differently in each group because their environments are different; after many generations new species can form   [1 each = 3]

Answers

Key Area 3.5

A Restricted-response questions (1 mark each)

1 a) enhance crop plant growth
  b) kill species that damage crop growth   [both]
2 increases the yield of crops
3 abnormally high growth of algae
4 species whose presence, absence or abundance suggests information about the state of the environment
5 mayfly; lichen...*(other possible answers)*
6 oxygen

B Extended-response questions (2 or 3 marks)

1 leached fertilisers increase algal growth in freshwater; algae start to die when light or nutrient levels become limiting; dying algae are food for aerobic bacteria; they multiply and deoxygenate water   [1 each = 3]
2 pesticides accumulate along food chains; build up in the bodies of carnivores; damage carnivores or their reproduction   [1 each = 3]
3 a) may have bigger yield; disease/pest resistance; cold/drought tolerance...*(other possible answers)*
  b) remove pests that reduce crop yield but reduce environmental impact... *(other possible answers)*   [1 each = 2]

Practice assessment: Unit 3 (40 marks)

Section A (10 marks)

1 The table below contains examples of factors affecting biodiversity in a Scottish mixed woodland ecosystem. Which line in the table below correctly identifies examples of biotic and abiotic factors?

	Biotic factors	Abiotic factors
A	Sparrowhawks are predators	Red deer graze low branches of deciduous trees
B	Soil has an acidic pH	Sparrowhawks are predators
C	Water is frozen for part of the winter	Soil has an acidic pH
D	Red deer graze low branches of deciduous trees	Water is frozen for part of the winter

2 Which statement describes biomes?
  A regions of the Earth with similar flora and fauna
  B levels of food chains with similar biodiversity
  C climate conditions that increase biodiversity
  D factors within ecosystems that affect flora and fauna

3 Which line in the table below describes two characteristics of mutations?

	Characteristic 1	Characteristic 2
A	Random	Spontaneous
B	Non-random	Predictable
C	Random	Predictable
D	Non-random	Spontaneous

4 The diagram below shows a pyramid of energy for a food chain.

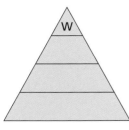

There is less energy at level W in the pyramid because:
  A the mass of individual organisms at level W is low
  B energy is stored in each level and is not passed on
  C the energy at level W is concentrated in a small number of organisms
  D energy is lost at each level in the food chain involved

5 There is concern about the adverse effect of intensive farming on ecosystems in the UK. Which of the following methods of increasing crop yields would be most likely to reduce the effects on ecosystems when used in conjunction with intensive farming?
  A using pesticides and planting GM crops
  B using fertilisers and pesticides
  C using biological control methods and fertilisers
  D planting GM crops and using biological control methods

6 What is the likely source of a selective advantage and the likely result for an organism?
   A mutation gives decreased chance of survival
   B mutation gives increased chance of survival
   C isolation barriers give decreased survival
   D isolation barriers give increased survival

7 The role of decomposers in ecosystems is to convert:
   A nitrogenous wastes to ammonium
   B ammonium to nitrogen gas
   C nitrogen gas to nitrate
   D nitrate to nitrite

8 The chart below shows the results of an investigation of the levels of insecticides in the muscle tissue of various farmland birds.

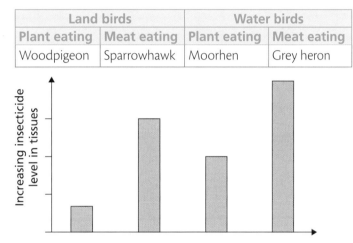

Land birds		Water birds	
Plant eating	**Meat eating**	**Plant eating**	**Meat eating**
Woodpigeon	Sparrowhawk	Moorhen	Grey heron

Increasing insecticide level in tissues

Which of the following conclusions is supported by the information in the chart?
   A insecticide damages water birds more than land birds
   B more insecticide is found in water habitats than in land habitats
   C meat-eaters accumulate more insecticide than plant-eaters
   D sparrowhawks eat woodpigeons

9 The information below refers to energy flow in a woodland ecosystem over a 24-hour period.
   ○ Light energy units available from the sun: 5 000 000
   ○ Energy units trapped by plants in photosynthesis: 10 000
   ○ Energy units released as heat during respiration: 9 000
   What percentage of available energy remained trapped in the ecosystem after this period?
   A 0.02%
   B 0.2%
   C 10%
   D 90%

10 The apparatus below was part of an experiment used to demonstrate the effects of SO_2 pollution on transpiration from a leafy shoot.

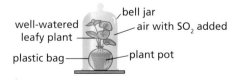

well-watered leafy plant

bell jar
air with SO_2 added
plastic bag — plant pot

A suitable control for this experiment would be provided by using the same set-up but:
   A using a black plastic bag
   B leaving out the leafy shoot

⇨

    C using SO_2-free air

    D leaving out the bell jar

Section B (30 marks)

1 The diagram below shows a food chain from a Scottish heather moorland ecosystem.

heather shoots → mountain hare → golden eagle

    a) Give **two** ways in which energy can be lost at each level of this food chain. (2)

    b) Food chains like this one can be represented as pyramids of number and of biomass. Describe **one** difference between these two pyramids. (1)

    c) The mountain hares are in competition for food with red grouse and with other mountain hares on heather moors. Copy and complete the table below to identify the type of competition in each case. (1)

Organism	Type of competition involved
Red grouse	
Other mountain hares	

2 The diagram below represents part of the nitrogen cycle in an area of agricultural land.

    a) Give the form of nitrogen shown at **X**, which is taken up by the plants and converted into proteins. (1)

    b) Give the term used to describe the action of bacteria at **Y** in the diagram. (1)

    c) (i) Describe the role of nitrogen-fixing bacteria in the nitrogen cycle. (1)

        (ii) Give two habitats in which these species of bacteria can be found. (1)

3 An investigation into the distribution of the alga *Pleurococcus* on the bark around the trunk of a mature tree was undertaken. Eight quadrats were placed around the circumference of the tree and the percentage of each occupied by the alga was measured. At the same stations on the tree, sample tubes were used to collect the moisture run-off from the bark in a 24-hour period. The results are shown in the table below.

Station	Moisture run-off from the bark (cm³ of water collected in a sample tube taped to the bark at each station per 24-hour period)	*Pleurococcus* (% cover)
1	0.5	24
2	0.8	32
3	1.2	54
4	1.8	80
5	1.9	85
6	2.1	98
7	1.6	65
8	0.8	30

⇨

⇨

   a) On a piece of graph paper, plot a line graph to show the distribution of *Pleurococcus* against the moisture run-off from the bark. (2SSI)

   b) Give the relationship between surface water run-off and the density of *Pleurococcus* on the bark of this tree. (1SSI)

   c) Suggest how the reliability of the results for moisture run-off from the bark could be improved. (1SSI)

   d) Calculate the percentage increase in the run-off between the lowest and highest values. (1SSI)

4 The following list refers to stages in an evolutionary process:

   1 Natural selection

   2 Mutation

   3 Isolation

   a) The diagram below shows the stages in the process and its end result. Copy the diagram and add numbers to the boxes to show the order in which the stages would normally occur. (1)

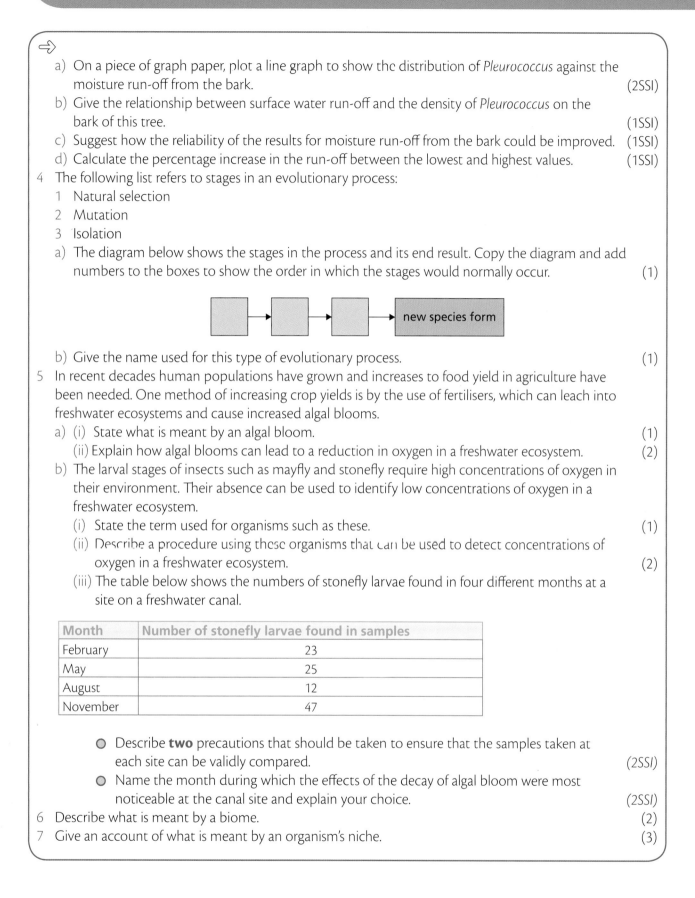

   b) Give the name used for this type of evolutionary process. (1)

5 In recent decades human populations have grown and increases to food yield in agriculture have been needed. One method of increasing crop yields is by the use of fertilisers, which can leach into freshwater ecosystems and cause increased algal blooms.

   a) (i) State what is meant by an algal bloom. (1)

      (ii) Explain how algal blooms can lead to a reduction in oxygen in a freshwater ecosystem. (2)

   b) The larval stages of insects such as mayfly and stonefly require high concentrations of oxygen in their environment. Their absence can be used to identify low concentrations of oxygen in a freshwater ecosystem.

      (i) State the term used for organisms such as these. (1)

      (ii) Describe a procedure using these organisms that can be used to detect concentrations of oxygen in a freshwater ecosystem. (2)

      (iii) The table below shows the numbers of stonefly larvae found in four different months at a site on a freshwater canal.

Month	Number of stonefly larvae found in samples
February	23
May	25
August	12
November	47

      ○ Describe **two** precautions that should be taken to ensure that the samples taken at each site can be validly compared. (2SSI)

      ○ Name the month during which the effects of the decay of algal bloom were most noticeable at the canal site and explain your choice. (2SSI)

6 Describe what is meant by a biome. (2)

7 Give an account of what is meant by an organism's niche. (3)

Answers to practice assessment: Unit 3

Section A

1 D, 2 A, 3 A, 4 D, 5 D, 6 B, 7 A, 8 C, 9 A, 10 C

Section B

1 a) heat; movement; undigested
       material   [any 2]
    b) numbers show populations at each level;
        biomass shows total mass of organisms at
        each level   [both]
    c) interspecific
        intraspecific   [both]
2 a) nitrate
    b) denitrifying/denitrification
    c) (i) convert nitrogen to nitrate
        (ii) soil; root nodules   [both]
3 a) scales and labels
        plots and line   [1 each = 2]
    b) as moisture run-off from the bark
        increases, the density/% cover of
        Pleurococcus increases
    c) repeating the experiment and calculating
        an average
    d) 320%

4 a) 3 → 2 → 1
    b) speciation
5 a) (i) unusually high growth of algae in a
            body of water
        (ii) algal bloom dies; dead algae
            decomposed by aerobic bacteria,
            which use up oxygen   [1 each = 2]
    b) (i) pollution/biological indicators
        (ii) take samples in the river; count
            larvae; relate larvae to oxygen
            level   [all 3 = 2, 2/1 = 1]
        (iii) same sampling method; same time
            spent on process; same weather
            conditions   [any 2 = 2]
            August; lowest stonefly count
            indicates lowest oxygen level   [both]
6 region of the Earth's surface with similar
   climate, fauna, flora   [all 3 = 2, 2/1 = 1]
7 role played in habitat; what organism eats
   and what eats it; what resources it requires
   and what it adds to the habitat   [1 each = 3]

Skills of Scientific Inquiry

The questions within the Key Areas of this book all test knowledge. This section covers the skills of scientific inquiry and includes questions to test these. We have given three different approaches to working with these science skills and recommend that you use all three.

- The first approach simply provides sets of hints and tips on answering science skills questions.
- The second approach goes through the skills one by one and gives you some exam-style questions to try. There is a grid on page 137 that shows which skills are tested in the parts of each question. The answers are given on pages 147–149.
- The third approach gives an example of a scientific investigation and breaks it down into its component skills. There are questions on each skill area. The answers are on page 149.

Approach 1: hints and tips

These are divided into the main skill areas but those directly related to **experimental skills** have been grouped together. Under **processing of information** we have shown how to tackle calculations involving percentage, ratio and average.

Tips on selecting information (from graphs)

- On graphs, the variable being investigated is on the *x*-axis and what is being measured is on the *y*-axis.
- Watch out for graphs with a double *y*-axis – these are tricky! The two *y*-axes often have different scales to increase the difficulty. You must take care to read the question and then the graph carefully to ensure that you are reading the correct *y*-axis.
- Work out the value of the smallest square on both scales before trying to read actual values from graphs.
- If you are asked to calculate an increase or decrease between points on a graph, you should use a ruler to help accuracy – draw pencil lines on the actual graph if this helps.
- When you are asked to describe a trend it is essential that you quote the values of the appropriate points and use the exact labels given on the axes in your answer. You must use the correct units in your description.

Tips on presenting information

- The most common question in this area requires students to present information that has been provided in a table as a graph – usually a line graph or sometimes a bar chart.
- Read the question to check if a line graph or a bar chart is required – the question will usually tell you.
- Marks are given for providing scales, labelling the axes correctly and plotting the data points. Line graphs require points to be joined with straight lines using a ruler. Bar charts need to have the bars drawn precisely using a ruler.
- The graph labels should be identical to the table headings and units. Copy them exactly, leaving nothing out.
- You need to decide which variable is to be plotted on each axis. The data for the variable under investigation is placed in the left column of a data table and should be scaled on the *x*-axis. The right column in a data table provides the label and data for the *y*-axis. You will lose a mark if these are reversed.
- You must select suitable scales so that at least half of the graph grid provided is used otherwise a mark will be deducted. The value of the divisions on the scales you choose should allow you to plot all points accurately.
- Make sure that your scales extend beyond the highest data points.
- The scale must rise in regular steps. At National 5 level the examiners may test you on this by deliberately skipping one of these values that they have given you to plot in the table. Watch out for this deliberate change in the data, which is designed to check your care in plotting.
- Be careful to include one or both zeros at the origin if appropriate. It is acceptable for a scale to start with a value other than zero if this suits the data.
- Take great care to plot each point accurately using a cross or a dot and then connect them exactly using a ruler.
- Do not plot zero or connect the points back to the origin unless zero is actually included in the data table. If 0 is there you must plot it.
- When drawing a bar graph ensure that the bars are the same width. Remember to include a key if the data require it.
- If you make a mistake in a graph, another piece of graph paper is provided at the end of your exam paper.

Tips on processing information: tackling the common calculations

Percentages

Expressing a number as a %

The number required as a percentage is divided by the total and then multiplied by 100, as shown:

$$\frac{\text{number wanted as a \%}}{\text{total}} \times 100$$

Percentage change: increase or decrease

First, calculate the increase or decrease. Then, express this value as a percentage:

$$\frac{\text{change}}{\text{original starting value}} \times 100$$

Ratios

These questions usually require you to express the values given or being compared as a simple whole number ratio.

First you need to obtain the values for the ratio from the data provided in the table or graph. Take care that you present the ratio values in the order they are stated in the question. Then simplify them, first by dividing the larger number by the smaller one then dividing the smaller one by itself. However, if this does not give a whole number then you need to find another number that will divide into both of them. For example, 21:14 cannot be simplified by dividing 21 by 14 since this would not give a whole number. You must then look for another number to divide into both, in this case 7. This would simplify the ratio to 3:2, which cannot be simplified any further.

Averages

Add up the values provided and then divide the total by the number of values given.

Tips on experimental skills of planning and designing

Questions designed to test your skills in this area require you to discuss aspects such as reliability, variables and fairness, validity, controls, measurements required, sources of error and suggested improvements. These questions often take the forms shown below.

- Give a reason for the experiment being repeated.
  - To improve the reliability of experiments and the results obtained, the experiment should be repeated.
- Give one precaution taken to ensure that the results would be valid.
  - To improve validity, only the one variable being investigated should be altered while the other variables should be kept constant.
- Describe a suitable control.
  - The control should be identical to the original experiment apart from the one factor being investigated.

- Explain why a control experiment was necessary.
  - A control experiment allows a comparison to be made and allows you to attribute any change or difference in the results to the factor or variable being altered.
- Why is it good experimental procedure to…?
  - If the effect of temperature on enzyme activity is being investigated, it is good practice to allow solutions of enzyme and substrate to reach the required temperature before mixing them to ensure that the reaction starts at the experimental temperature.
  - It is good experimental practice to use percentage change when you are comparing results because this allows a fair comparison to be made when the starting values in an investigation are different.

Precautions to minimise errors include washing apparatus such as beakers or syringes, or using different ones if the experiment involves different chemicals or concentrations. This prevents cross-contamination.

Questions regarding procedures that ask why the experiment was left for a certain time require you to state that this is to allow enough time for particular events to occur. These events could include the following:

- diffusion or absorption of substances into tissue
- growth taking place
- the effects of substances becoming visible
- a reaction occurring

Experimental situations can often be modified to test different variables. If you are asked about this, think about how to alter different variables while keeping the original variable constant. For example, the *Cabomba* bubbler is often used to investigate variable light intensities. If light intensity was kept constant then the bubbler could be used to investigate temperature by exposing it to different temperatures while keeping the light intensity constant.

The context of scientific inquiry questions will usually be unfamiliar to you but the techniques and tips we have given should apply to most situations.

> **Hints & tips** ★
>
> *Examples of the variables that need to be controlled and kept constant to ensure results would be valid include temperature, pH, concentrations, mass, volume, length, number, surface area and type of tissue, depending on the actual experiment.*

> **Hints & tips** ★
>
> *If you are asked to describe a suitable control, make sure that you describe it in full.*

> **Hints & tips** ★
>
> *Watch out for the questions that refer to dry mass. Since the water content of tissues is variable and can change from day to day, dry mass is often used when comparing masses of tissues that are expected to change under experimental conditions.*

Approach 2: skill by skill

The basic skills that can be tested in your exam are listed in the table on page 137. We have provided six practice questions (1–6), two from each Unit, which cover all the skill areas between them. The table also shows the parts of the practice questions where you can find each skill tested. It is probably better to try the whole of each question in turn. If you find particular difficulty with any part of a question you can use the table to identify the skill area that needs further work.

Skill area	Category within skill area	Practice questions					
		Unit 1 Q1	Unit 1 Q2	Unit 2 Q3	Unit 2 Q4	Unit 3 Q5	Unit 3 Q6
1 Selecting information...	...from a line graph or bar chart	–	–	–	f	–	bi2
	...from a pie chart or table	–	–	–	–	–	bi1
2 Presenting information...	...as a line graph	d	d	a	–	a	–
3 Processing information...	...as a ratio	–	–	d	–	f	–
	...as an average	–	–	–	g	–	–
	...as a percentage	–	–	c	h	g	–
	...as a percentage change	–	–	f	–	–	–
	...by general calculation [addition, subtraction, multiplying and dividing]	–	–	b, e	–	h	–
4 Planning and designing	Planning: aim, hypothesis, dependent and independent variables	–	–	–	a	b	–
	Designing: apparatus, replicates, other variables and controls	a, b, c, g	c, e, g, j	–	b, c, d, j	c, e, i	ai
5 Predicting and generalising	Predicting	e	b	g	–	–	biii
	Generalising	–	a	–	–	–	–
6 Concluding and explaining	Concluding	f	h	h	i	d	bii
	Explaining	–	b	–	–	–	–
7 Evaluating	Identifying source of error	–	i	–	e	–	aii
	Suggesting improvement	–	f, g	–	e	–	aii

Unit 1 Cell biology

Question 1   Key Area 1.2   Osmosis ?

An investigation was carried out into the movement of water through a selectively permeable membrane by the process of osmosis. Apparatus was set up as shown in the diagram below and the distance moved by the liquid in the glass tube recorded after 1 hour.

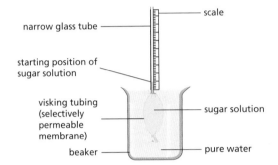

The experiment was repeated with different concentrations of sugar solution. The results are shown in the following table.

Concentration of sugar solution (%)	Distance moved by sugar solution in 1 hour (mm)
0.5	3
1.0	6
2.0	12
3.0	18
3.5	21

1 a) Identify **one** variable, not already mentioned, that should be kept constant during the investigation. (1)

b) Explain why the visking tubing bag was left for 1 hour in each solution before measuring the distance moved by the solution. (1)

c) Suggest how the reliability of the results could be improved. (1)

d) On a piece of graph paper, copy and complete the line graph below to show the distance moved by the solution in 1 hour against the concentration of the sugar solution. (2)

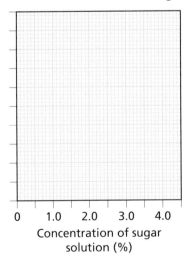

Concentration of sugar solution (%)

e) From the results, predict the distance a 4% sugar solution would be expected to move in 1 hour and justify your prediction. (2)

f) Give a conclusion about the concentration of the sugar solution that can be drawn from the results obtained. (1)

g) Describe how the apparatus used in this investigation could be adapted to investigate the effect of temperature on osmosis. (2)

Question 2   Key Area 1.8   Respiration ?

In an investigation into the effect of temperature on the rate of respiration by yeast, sets of apparatus, as shown in the diagram, were set up at different temperatures. The yeast was allowed to respire at each temperature for 1 hour and the gas formed collected and measured.

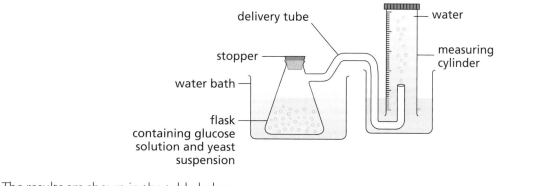

The results are shown in the table below.

Temperature (°C)	10	20	30	40	50
Volume of gas produced in 1 hour (cm³)	9	18	36	48	5

2 a) Describe the relationship between the temperature and the volume of gas produced in 1 hour. (1)

b) Predict the volume of gas that would be collected in 1 hour if the investigation was repeated at 25°C. Explain your answer. (2)

c) Describe the control flasks that would be set up to show that the gas was produced due to activity of the yeast and to no other factor. (1)

d) On a piece of graph paper, copy and complete the line graph to show the volume of gas produced in 1 hour for each temperature. (2)

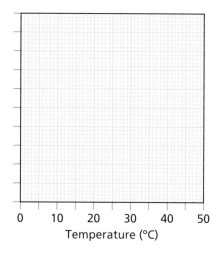

Temperature (°C)

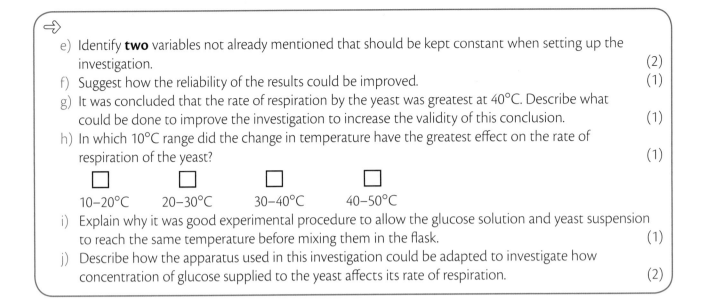

e) Identify **two** variables not already mentioned that should be kept constant when setting up the investigation. (2)

f) Suggest how the reliability of the results could be improved. (1)

g) It was concluded that the rate of respiration by the yeast was greatest at 40°C. Describe what could be done to improve the investigation to increase the validity of this conclusion. (1)

h) In which 10°C range did the change in temperature have the greatest effect on the rate of respiration of the yeast? (1)

☐   ☐   ☐   ☐

10–20°C   20–30°C   30–40°C   40–50°C

i) Explain why it was good experimental procedure to allow the glucose solution and yeast suspension to reach the same temperature before mixing them in the flask. (1)

j) Describe how the apparatus used in this investigation could be adapted to investigate how concentration of glucose supplied to the yeast affects its rate of respiration. (2)

Unit 2 Multicellular organisms

Question 3 Key Area 2.6c Gas exchange ?

The effect of changing the carbon dioxide concentration in inhaled air on an individual's breathing was investigated. The average volume of air inhaled each minute at different concentrations of carbon dioxide was measured. The results are shown in the table below.

Carbon dioxide concentration in inhaled air (%)	0	2	4	6	8
Average volume of air inhaled (litres per minute)	8	12	16	24	60

3 a) On a piece of graph paper, copy and complete the line graph of CO_2 concentration in inhaled air against the average volume of air inhaled. (2)

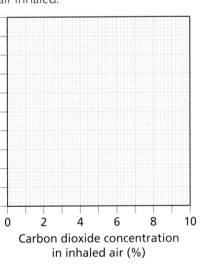

Carbon dioxide concentration
in inhaled air (%)

b) State the number of times greater the average volume of air inhaled per minute was after the carbon dioxide concentration was increased from 2% to 8%. (1)

c) Calculate the average volume of carbon dioxide entering the lungs each minute when the carbon dioxide concentration in the air was 4%. (1)

⇨

d) Calculate the increases in the average volume of air inhaled per minute when the carbon dioxide concentration changed from 0% to 2% and from 6% to 8%. Express these increases as a simple whole number ratio. (1)

e) Calculate the average volume of air inhaled per hour when the carbon dioxide concentration of inhaled air was 2%. (1)

f) Calculate the percentage change in the average volume of air inhaled per minute when the carbon dioxide concentration increased from 4% to 6%. (1)

g) From the results, predict the average volume of air inhaled per minute when the carbon dioxide concentration was 3%, and justify your prediction. (1)

h) Describe the relationship between the carbon dioxide concentration in inhaled air and the average volume of air inhaled. (1)

Question 4   Key Area 2.6c Digestion   ?

An investigation was set up to examine the effects of stirring on the digestion of protein. The experiment was set up as shown below.

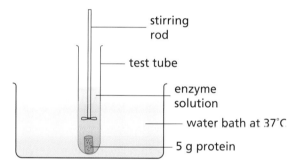

The protein present in each tube was removed and its mass measured every hour. The results are shown in the table and graph below.

		Time (hours)					
		0	1	2	3	4	5
Mass of protein present in each tube (g)	Not stirred	5.0	4.7	4.3	3.8	3.2	2.5
	Stirred	5.0	4.4	3.6	2.6	1.4	0.0

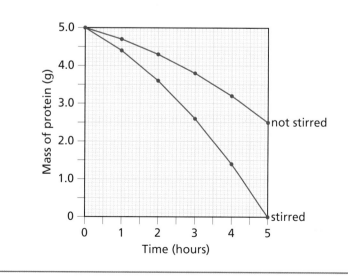

⇨

141

4 a) Name the independent variable in this investigation. (1)
   b) Name **one** variable, not already mentioned, that would need to be kept the same in each tube at the start of the investigation. (1)
   c) Suggest how the investigation could be improved to provide a more reliable measurement of the difference that stirring makes. (1)
   d) Describe the contents of the control tube that would be needed to show the effect of stirring on the digestion of protein. (1)
   e) Identify a source of error in the measurement of the protein removed from the tube that may have resulted in a higher mass than was actually recorded, and suggest an improvement. (2)
   f) Give the mass of protein that might be expected to remain undigested in the unstirred tube after 1 hour and 30 minutes. (1)
   g) Calculate the average hourly decrease in the mass of the protein over the 5-hour period in the tube with no stirring. (1)
   h) Calculate the mass of protein that had been digested after 3 hours in the stirred tube as a percentage. (1)
   i) Give a conclusion that can be drawn from the results obtained. (1)
   j) Describe how the apparatus used in this experiment could be adapted to investigate the effect of temperature on the digestion of protein. (2)

Unit 3 Life on Earth

Question 5   Key Area 3.2 Competition ?

Six Petri dishes were set up to investigate the effect of intraspecific competition on the percentage of cress seedlings surviving after 5 days. Each dish contained a thin layer of wet cotton wool with a different number of seeds placed evenly across its surface.

The dish containing five seeds is shown in the diagram below.

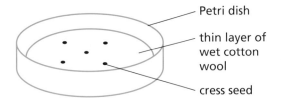

The results of this investigation are shown in the table below.

Dish	Number of seeds sown	Seedlings surviving after 5 days (%)
A	5	100
B	10	100
C	20	95
D	40	80
E	60	70
F	80	60

5 a) On a piece of graph paper, copy and complete the line graph to show the number of seeds sown against percentage of seedlings surviving after 5 days. (2)

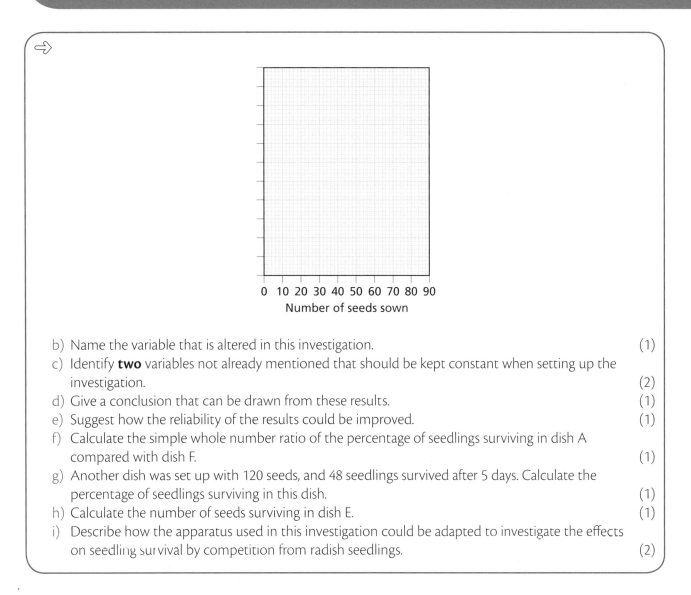

0 10 20 30 40 50 60 70 80 90
Number of seeds sown

b) Name the variable that is altered in this investigation. (1)
c) Identify **two** variables not already mentioned that should be kept constant when setting up the investigation. (2)
d) Give a conclusion that can be drawn from these results. (1)
e) Suggest how the reliability of the results could be improved. (1)
f) Calculate the simple whole number ratio of the percentage of seedlings surviving in dish A compared with dish F. (1)
g) Another dish was set up with 120 seeds, and 48 seedlings survived after 5 days. Calculate the percentage of seedlings surviving in this dish. (1)
h) Calculate the number of seeds surviving in dish E. (1)
i) Describe how the apparatus used in this investigation could be adapted to investigate the effects on seedling survival by competition from radish seedlings. (2)

Question 6   Key Area 3.3   Sampling ?

6 a) A comparison was made between the types of invertebrate animals living on the branches and leaves on an oak tree with those living on a cherry tree. Samples were collected by tree beating, as shown below.

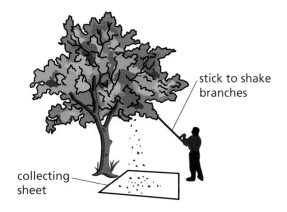

stick to shake
branches

collecting
sheet

(i) Give **two** variables that should be kept constant to make the comparison between samples from the two trees valid when using this technique. (1)

⇨

(ii) The samples collected were not representative of all the invertebrates living on the trees. Suggest **one** feature of the sampling technique that could have led to this problem and give **one** improvement that could allow a more representative sample to be taken. (2)

(b) An investigation was carried out into the effect of light intensity on the distribution of a plant species. At eight different sampling stations in a garden, the average light intensity was measured and the percentage ground cover of the plant was recorded. The results are shown in the table and graph below.

Sampling station	Average light intensity (lux)
1	1000
2	750
3	400
4	400
5	500
6	600
7	2000
8	1200

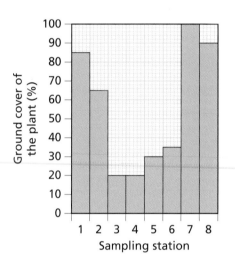

(i) 1) State the light intensity in the garden where the ground cover of the plant was 100%. (1)

2) State the percentage ground cover of the plant when the light intensity was 750 lux. (1)

(ii) Describe the relationship between light intensity and percentage ground cover of the plant. (1)

(iii) Predict the percentage ground cover of the plant in conditions in which the average light intensity is 450 lux. (1)

The *Cabomba* bubbler (see page 30)

Read through the information about the experiment below and then work through the skill areas listed, trying to comment on the questions in each category.

1   The apparatus was set up as shown in the diagram.

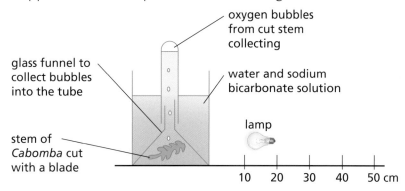

oxygen bubbles from cut stem collecting

glass funnel to collect bubbles into the tube

water and sodium bicarbonate solution

lamp

stem of *Cabomba* cut with a blade

10   20   30   40   50 cm

2   The plant was exposed to bright light and allowed to bubble for 10 minutes before the experiment was started.
3   The light intensity was altered by moving the lamp further away from the plant, and the rate of photosynthesis was measured by counting the number of bubbles of oxygen coming from the cut plant stem in a set period of time at each distance.
4   The experiment was repeated at each distance and the two results averaged.
5   The results obtained are shown in the table below.

Light intensity (distance of lamp from plant in cm)	Average rate of photosynthesis (bubbles of oxygen produced per minute)
10	20
20	20
30	15
40	10
50	5

Planning experiments and designing experiments

This is about confirming the aim of an experiment and suggesting a likely hypothesis, choosing apparatus, thinking about the dependent variable and deciding what to measure. Designing is closely related to planning but involves details of how often to measure, which variables need to be controlled and how to do this. It also involves anticipating possible errors and trouble-shooting these.

Q1   Suggest what the aim of the experiment was.
Q2   Suggest a hypothesis that would go with this aim.
Q3   Why is a water plant used?
Q4   Why is sodium bicarbonate solution used? (Hint: this solution acts as a source of carbon dioxide.)

Q5   Why are the bubbles counted? What's in the bubbles and why is this important?

Q6   Why should the plant be allowed to bubble for a while before the experiment starts? (Hint: *Cabomba* stems have natural air spaces, which help the plant float in water.)

Q7   How is light intensity altered?

Q8   Which vital piece of apparatus is missing from the diagram on page 145? (Hint: bubbles per *minute* are given in the results!)

Q9   Which variables should have been controlled?

Q10 Why was the experiment repeated at each light intensity?

Selecting information

This is about using a source such as a table or line graph to extract particular pieces of information. This can be simply reading off a value. The skill requires knowledge about labels, scales and units.

Q11 How many bubbles of oxygen are produced per minute when the lamp is 30 cm from the plant?

Q12 How far away from the plant was the lamp when the bubbling rate was 5 bubbles per minute?

Presenting information

This is about taking some information and presenting it in a different and more useful form. A common type of presentation might be to take information from a table and present it as a line graph. The skill requires knowledge of labels, scales and units as well as careful drawing using a ruler and plotting accurately.

Q13 Draw a line graph to show the rate of photosynthesis against the light intensity. Be careful to have the scale of light intensity going from least to most intense – think about it!

Processing information

This is often about working with numerical data and using calculations to convert a lot of data into a simple form.

Q14 What is the ratio of number of bubbles produced with the light at 10 cm to those produced at 50 cm?

Q15 What is the average rate of bubbling over all of the trials?

Q16 What is the percentage increase in the rate of bubbling when the lamp is moved from 50 cm to 20 cm from the plant?

Predicting and generalising

Predicting is about taking an experimental result and imagining what would happen if a variable changed. Generalising is about looking at experimental results and trying to find a rule that would hold true in all situations.

Q17 How would bubbling be affected by moving the lamp to 5 cm and 60 cm away?

Q18 How would you expect the results to differ if a different species of water plant was used?

Q19 How would you expect the glucose concentration in the plant to change during the experiment?

Concluding and explaining

Concluding involves making a statement about the relationship between variables in an experiment. Explaining is about using knowledge to understand why a result has been obtained.

Q20 How is the rate of photosynthesis affected by light intensity?

Q21 Explain the results in terms of your knowledge about the light-dependent stage of photosynthesis and limiting factors in photosynthesis.

Evaluating

Evaluating is looking critically at an experiment and deciding if it is likely to be valid and if its results can be relied on; it is about looking for potential sources of error. Evaluating also involves suggesting improvements to an experiment that might remove sources of error in future experimental repeats.

Q22 What sources of error might be present – how would you prove the bubbles were really oxygen?

Q23 Are all the bubbles the same size – does it matter? Is there a better way to measure the gas coming off?

Q24 How could the exact distance of the lamp from the plant be made certain? Is there a better way of changing light intensity?

Q25 Is any other light source present? Does that matter and how could you control this?

Q26 What factors, other than light intensity, might be limiting photosynthesis?

Q27 How reliable is one set of results with one plant and one lamp?

Q28 How could this experiment be improved? Make a list!

Q29 Which other factors that affect photosynthesis could be investigated using the *Cabomba* bubbler apparatus? How could you adapt the experimental set-up to investigate one of these?

Scientific inquiry skills answers

Skill by skill

1 a) volume of sugar solution; temperature of water; volume of water   [any 1]

   b) allow enough time for osmosis to be completed

   c) repeat experiment for each concentration and then obtain average

   d) *y*-axis scale and label = 1; correctly plotted and points connected using a ruler = 1

   e) 24 mm; distance moved by sugar solution increases by 3 mm per hour for every 0.5% increase in sugar concentration *or* 6 mm per hour for every 1% increase in sugar concentration

   f) as concentration of sugar solution increases, distance moved by sugar solution increases

   g) repeat with same apparatus with one sugar concentration; but at a range of temperatures

2 a) as temperature increases, volume of gas produced in 1 hour increases up to 40°C then starts to decrease between 40°C and 50°C

   b) 27 cm^3 = 1; volume of gas produced doubled between 20°C and 30°C or increased by 18 cm^3 and so at 25°C would have increased by 9 cm^3

$\Rightarrow$

⇨

c) exactly the same set up but lacking the yeast suspension

d) y-axis scale and label = 1; correctly plotted and points connected using a ruler = 1

e) volume of glucose solution; concentration of glucose solution; volume of yeast suspension; concentration of yeast suspension; type of yeast; pH   [any 2]

f) repeat each experiment for each temperature and then obtain an average

g) repeat experiment using a narrower range of temperatures around 40°C or within suitable range (35–45°C)

h) 40–50°C

i) to be sure that respiration was taking place at correct experimental temperature or if they had not, respiration could have been taking place at lower temperature

j) repeat experiment at same temperature; with a range of glucose concentrations

3 a) y-axis scale and label = 1; correctly plotted and points connected using a ruler = 1

b) 5 times

c) 0.64 litres

d) 1:9

e) 720 litres

f) 50%

g) 14 litres = 1
increase of 4 litres between 2% and 4% carbon dioxide concentration, so at 3% you would expect increase of 2 litres to have occurred = 1

h) as carbon dioxide concentration increases, average volume of air inhaled increases

4 a) stirring

b) pH/volume of enzyme solution; concentration of enzyme solution; type of enzyme; surface area of protein

c) repeat each experiment and obtain an average or measure the decrease in the mass of protein every 30 minutes or other suitable duration

d) exactly the same volume and concentration of enzyme, mass of protein

e) error – surface liquid/solution was also being measured and contributing to the mass = 1
improvement – blot/dry between each measurement = 1

f) 4.5 g

g) 0.5 g per hour

h) 48%

i) stirring increases the rate at which the protein is digested or improves the digestion of protein

j) repeat experiment; at range of temperatures but with no stirring

5 a) y-axis scale and label = 1; correctly plotted and points connected using a ruler = 1

b) number of seeds; spacing between seeds   [either]

c) temperature; mass or depth or thickness of cotton wool; volume of water; type of seed   [any 2]

d) as number of seeds in each dish increases, percentage of seedlings surviving after 5 days decreases

e) repeat each experiment with each number of seeds and then obtain an average

f) 5:3

g) 40%

h) 42

i) keep number of cress seeds constant but add increasing numbers of raddish seeds

6 a) (i) same height on the tree; same size of branch; same strength or duration of beating, or number of beats; same size or surface area of collecting sheet; same time of day; same weather conditions   [any 2 = 1]

(ii) error – not all invertebrates are dislodged or some have not been shaken loose; sample taken from same height on tree; flying insects could escape; some invertebrates could crawl off sheet   [any 1 = 1]
improvement – examine branches and leaves by hand or remove invertebrates by hand; sample at all heights; collect organisms from sheet quickly   [any 1 = 1]   ⇨

⇨

b) (i) 1) 2000 lux 2) 65%
(ii) as light intensity increases, percentage ground cover of plant increases
(iii) 25%

Through an example: the *Cabomba* bubbler

Q1 To investigate the effects of changing light intensity on the rate of photosynthesis

Q2 Increasing light intensity will increase the rate of photosynthesis.

Q3 Produces bubbles of oxygen, which are a product of photosynthesis and can be easily seen and counted

Q4 Photosynthesis requires CO_2, which is absent in tap water; the bicarbonate solution breaks down to give CO_2; in natural waters, respiration of living organisms would add CO_2 to the water.

Q5 It is a measure of oxygen produced; oxygen is a photosynthesis product.

Q6 Better to ensure that any trapped air is released first

Q7 Moving the lamp nearer to the plant increases the intensity of the light.

Q8 A stop clock or watch

Q9 Temperature of plant; concentration of CO_2 available; the plant

Q10 It increases the reliability of the results.

Q11 15 bubbles

Q12 50 cm

Q13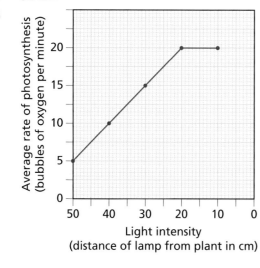

Q14 4:1

Q15 14 bubbles per minute

Q16 300%

Q17 At 5 cm, no increase in the rate of photosynthesis compared with 10 cm; at 60 cm, lower than that at 50 cm

Q18 No real reason to think it would be different – it would need to be investigated.

Q19 You would expect an increase at higher intensities because glucose is another product of photosynthesis.

Q20 As light intensity increases, the rate of photosynthesis increases up to 20 cm, after which increases in light intensity cause no further increase in rate of photosynthesis.

Q21 Light intensity is a limiting factor, so it should limit the rate at low intensities; at high intensities other factors could start to limit photosynthesis.

Q22 The bubbles might not be pure oxygen; the gas could be collected and tested with a glowing splint.

Q23 It does matter and the bubbles are probably not the same size. The gas could be collected in an inverted measuring cylinder to measure the volume of oxygen produced.

Q24 By ensuring that distance is measured accurately to the glass of the bulb. Would a dimmer control be better? Could a photographer's light meter be used?

Q25 Other light does matter. The experiment could be carried out in a darkened room.

Q26 Temperature and CO_2 concentration

Q27 Probably not reliable enough – more plants would be needed.

Q28 There are several improvements that would make this experiment better!

Q29 Temperature and CO_2 concentration. By keeping light intensity constant, it would be possible to alter either temperature or CO_2 concentration.

Your Assignment

The assignment is a task, which is based on a research investigation that you have carried out, mainly in class time. *You choose the topic* to be studied and then investigate or research the underlying biology and any impact it may have on society or the environment.

The assignment will assess the application of skills of scientific inquiry and related biology knowledge and understanding that you have developed throughout the course.

The investigation is supervised by teachers who should supply you with the *Instructions for Candidates* document published by SQA. You will have to write up the work in the form of a report of between 500 and 800 words under *controlled assessment conditions* at a later stage. During your write up you will have access to your investigation notes but not a draft copy of your assignment report.

The report will be *marked out of 20 marks* with 14 of the marks being for scientific inquiry skills and 6 marks for the application of knowledge.

The assignment is marked by the SQA and contributes 20% to the overall grade for your course.

Outline of the stages in the assignment

Research stage

1 Selection of a topic

The topic should be related to a National 5 Biology Key Area. Your teacher will probably give you some ideas to choose from. Make sure you choose something you are interested in and that you understand. The lists below show some suggested topics from the three Units – don't feel you need to use any of these.

Unit 1 Cell biology

- Industrial uses of osmosis, such as in power generation and desalination
- Cell production by cell culture
- Use of DNA sequencing in forensics
- Use of enzymes in industry
- Current issues with GM foods
- Industrial use of fermenters

Unit 2   Multicellular organisms

- Use of mitotic index in assessing human tumours
- Uses of stem cells in producing replacement organs
- Production of artificial blood
- Uses of cells from tissue culture for the development of new medicines or other uses
- Overuse of antibiotics in medicine or farming
- Sports drinks and rehydration

Unit 3   Life on Earth

- Filtration of domestic effluent or industrial waste using natural reed beds
- Stimulating oceanic algal growth to reduce global CO_2 concentrations in the atmosphere
- Increasing human dependence on fertilisers and pesticides to produce sufficient food
- Use of myxomatosis virus to control rabbit populations
- Use and effects of DDT in the past and at present
- General use of biological control methods as an alternative to pesticides
- Food security

2   Planning the investigation

Think carefully about your task – what do you already know? Where can you find out more? Focus on any applications and on the impact the content of your chosen topic has on society or the environment.

Ensure that you have a clear aim for the assignment and are sure of the reason you chose your topic. Be clear about the process you will adopt and how you may finally present your findings, including any data or information that you collect.

3   Identifying sources

You can use books, magazines, journals, monographs, the Internet, resource packs, personal interviews, visits to appropriate facilities or any other suitable approach that your teacher agrees with. Choose media that you have easy access to. Your school library and librarian might be able to help. You should choose suitable sources which are relevant, reliable and offer a balanced viewpoint.

4   Carrying out the investigation

As you work through various sources and extract relevant information, you will want to record anything of potential value. How will you record this material? Remember that you must include at least one graph, table, chart or diagram. You will need to compare information or data from at least two sources.

Be aware of the need to provide a balanced evaluation regarding the impact the topic you have studied may have on society or the environment.

This stage should be carried out mainly in class time and you will be allowed to take some of the material produced during this stage for use in the controlled assessment stage – *make sure you know what you will be taking in!* Remember that you cannot take in a draft copy of your assignment report.

5 Selecting and gathering relevant information

You will go through a process of selecting the most relevant, reliable and appropriate material to include in your final report. How will you organise your report? Do you need a contents page? Do you need sub-headings? How will you label your graphics and do they need captions?

Communication stage

Writing up your assignment report

You will have to write up your report under controlled conditions, with access to your notes. Be aware of the number of words (500–800) which is expected. It is also expected that your work will show literacy and numeracy skills. Here is a short checklist!

- Title
- Contents page
- Topic and aim clear
- Impact on society or environment clearly stated
- Spelling and grammar correct
- Divided up into coherent sections with sub-headings
- Relevant, reliable and unbiased material included
- Graphs and tables neatly presented, with labels, headings and units
- Statistical calculations (averages, percentages and ratios) accurate and clear
- Conclusion valid and justified
- Reference to at least two sources included

Your Exam

General exam revision: 20 top tips

These are very general tips and would apply to all your exams.

1 Start revising in good time.

Don't leave it until the last minute – this will make you panic and it will be impossible to learn. Make a revision timetable that counts down the weeks to go.

2 Work to a study plan.

Set up sessions of work spread through the weeks ahead. Make sure each session has a focus and a clear purpose. What will you study, when and why?

3 Make sure you know exactly when your exams are.

Get your exam dates from the SQA website and use the timetable builder tool to make up your own exam timetable. You will also get a personalised timetable from your school but this might not be until close to the exam period.

4 Make sure that you know the topics that make up each course.

Studying is easier if material is in chunks – why not use the SQA chunks? Ask your teacher for help on this if you are not sure.

5 Break the chunks up into even smaller bits.

The small chunks should be easier to cope with. Remember that they fit together to make larger ideas. Even the process of chunking down will help!

6 Ask yourself these key questions for each course.

Are all topics compulsory or are there choices? Which topics seem to come up time and time again? Which topics are your strongest and which are your weakest?

7 Make sure you know what to expect in the exam.

How is the paper structured? How much time is there for each question? What types of question are involved – multiple choice, restricted response, extended response?

8 There is no substitute for past papers – they are simply essential!

The last 4 years' papers for all Courses are on the SQA website – look for the past paper finder and download as PDF files. There are answers and mark schemes too.

9 **Use study methods that work well for you.**

People study and learn in different ways. Reading and looking at diagrams suits some people. Others prefer to listen and hear material – what about reading out loud or getting a friend or family member to do this for you? You could also record and play back material.

10 **There are only three ways to put material into your long-term memory:**
- practice – e.g. rehearsal, repeating
- organisation – e.g. making drawings, lists, diagrams, tables, memory aids
- elaborating – e.g. winding the material into a story or an imagined journey

11 **Learn actively.**

Most people prefer to learn actively – for example, making notes, highlighting, redrawing and redrafting, making up memory aids, writing past paper answers.

12 **Be an expert.**

Be sure to have a few areas in which you feel you are an expert. This often works because at least some of them will come up, which can boost confidence.

13 **Try some visual methods.**

Use symbols, diagrams, charts, flashcards, post-it notes etc. The brain takes in chunked images more easily than loads of text.

14 **Remember – practice makes perfect.**

Work on difficult areas again and again. Look and read – then test yourself. You cannot do this too much.

15 **Try past papers against the clock.**

Practise writing answers in a set time. As a rough guide, you should be able to score a mark per minute.

16 **Collaborate with friends.**

Test each other and talk about the material – this can really help. Two brains are better than one! It is amazing how talking about a problem can help you solve it.

17 **Know your weaknesses.**

Ask your teacher for help to identify what you don't know. If you are having trouble, it is probably with a difficult topic so your teacher will already be aware of this – most students will find it tough.

18 **Have your materials organised and ready.**

Know what is needed for each exam. Do you need a calculator or a ruler? Should you have pencils as well as pens? Will you need water or paper tissues?

19 **Make full use of school resources.**

Are there study classes available? Is the library open? When is the best time to ask for extra help? Can you borrow textbooks, study guides, past papers etc? Is school open for Easter revision?

20 **Keep fit and healthy!**

Mix study with relaxation, drink plenty of water, eat sensibly, and get fresh air and exercise – all these things will help more than you could imagine. If you are tired, sluggish or dehydrated, it is difficult to see how concentration is even possible.

National 5 Biology exam tips

These tips apply specifically to National 5 Biology. Remember that your assignment is worth 20 marks – the other 80 marks come from the examination.

Section A: multiple choice (20 marks)

- Do not spend more than *30 minutes* on this section.
- Answer on a grid. Make sure the grid has your name pre-printed on it.
- *Do not leave blanks* – complete the grid for each question as you work through.
- Try to answer each question in your head *without* looking at the options. If your answer is there, you are home and dry!
- If not certain, choose the answer that seemed most attractive on *first* reading the answer options.
- If you are guessing, try to eliminate options before making your guess. If you can eliminate three, you are left with the correct answer even if you do not recognise it!

Section B: restricted and extended response (60 marks)

- Spend about *90 minutes* on this section.
- Answer on the question paper. Try to write neatly and keep your answers on the support lines if possible – these are designed to take the full answer.
- Another clue to answer length is the mark allocation. Most questions are restricted to 1 mark and the answer can be quite short; if there are 2 or 3 marks available, your answer will need to be extended and may well have two, three or even four parts.
- The questions are usually laid out in unit sequence but remember that some questions are *designed* to cover more than one unit.

- Grade C (less demanding) questions usually start with 'State', 'Give' or 'Name'.
- Grade A (more demanding) questions begin with 'Explain' and 'Describe' and are likely to have more than one part to the full answer.
- Abbreviations like DNA and ATP are fine.
- Don't worry that some questions are in unfamiliar contexts. This is deliberate. Just keep calm and read the questions carefully.
- If a question contains a choice, be sure to spend enough time making the right choice.
- Remember to *use values from the graph* if you are asked to do so.
- Draw graphs using a ruler and use the data table headings for the axes labels.
- Look out for graphs with two *y*-axes – these need extra concentration as they can easily lead to mistakes.
- Answers to calculations will not usually have more than two decimal places.
- If there is a space for calculation given it is very likely that you will need to use it.
- Do not leave blanks. Have a go, using the language in the question if you can.

Glossary

The terms included here appear in the SQA Assessment Specification for National 5 Biology. They are defined here in the context of National 5. The Key Area in which a term first appears is given in brackets after each term.

Where a term has an unusual singular or plural, this is given in brackets with the definition.

You could make flashcards with the term on one side and the meaning on the other – a great resource for revision!

A, G, T, C and U (1.4) letters that represent the names of bases of DNA and mRNA

Abiotic (3.1) refers to physical factors, such as temperature and light intensity, that affect ecosystems

Active site (1.5) position on the surface of an enzyme molecule to which specific substrate molecules can bind

Active transport (1.2) transport of molecules against their concentration gradient

Adaptation (3.4) feature of an organism that helps it to survive

ADP and inorganic phosphate (1.8) substances that are combined to produce ATP

Aerobic (3.5) in the presence of, or involving the use of, oxygen

Aerobic respiration (1.1) release of energy from food by a cell using oxygen

Algal bloom (3.5) a seasonal abundance of algae

Allele (2.5) a form of a gene

Alveoli (2.6c) tiny sacs in lungs that form the gas exchange surface (*sing.* alveolus)

Amino acid (1.4) a building block of a protein molecule

Ammonium (3.2) NH_4; a nitrogen-containing waste product of decomposition

Anther (2.4) organ within a flower that produces pollen grains

Antibody (1.5) protein that is involved in defence in animals

Aorta (2.6b) main artery that carries oxygenated blood away from the heart in mammals

Artery (2.6b) general name for a blood vessel that carries blood away from the heart

Aseptic techniques (1.3) laboratory procedures designed to prevent contamination of pure cultures of microorganisms

ATP (1.7) adenosine triphosphate; a substance that transfers chemical energy in cells

Atria (2.6b) upper chambers of the heart, which receive blood from veins (*sing.* atrium)

Bacterial cell (1.1)   a tiny individual cell of a bacterium

Bases (1.4)   form the genetic code of DNA and mRNA

Biodiversity (3.1)   refers to the number and abundance of species

Biological control (3.5)   natural control of pests using natural predators, parasites or disease

Biome (3.1)   region of the planet with characteristic climate, flora and fauna

Biotic (3.1)   factor related to the biological aspects of an ecosystem such as predation and competition

Bond (1.4)   chemical link between atoms in a molecule

Brain (2.3a)   organ of the central nervous system of mammals where vital functions are coordinated

Capillaries (2.6b)   tiny blood vessels with walls one-cell thick where exchange of materials occurs

Carbohydrate (1.7)   a substance such as sugar, starch or glycogen, containing the elements carbon, hydrogen and oxygen

Carbon fixation stage (1.7)   second stage in photosynthesis in which ATP, hydrogen and carbon dioxide are involved in the production of sugar

Carnivore (3.2)   consumer which eats other animals

Cartilage (2.6c)   flexible tissue forming C-shaped rings in the trachea to keep the airway open

Catalyst (1.5)   a substance that speeds up a chemical reaction by reducing the energy required to start it

Cell membrane (1.1)   selectively permeable membrane enclosing the cell cytoplasm and controlling the entry and exit of materials

Cell wall (1.1)   supports and prevents cells from bursting; plant, fungal and bacterial walls have different structures and chemical compositions

Cellulose (1.1)   structural carbohydrate of which plant cell walls are composed

Central nervous system (CNS) (2.3a)   part of the nervous system made up of the brain and spinal cord

Cerebellum (2.3a)   part of the brain that controls balance and coordination of movement

Cerebrum (2.3a)   large folded part of the brain that controls conscious responses, memory, thought, intelligence and emotions

Chlorophyll (1.7)   green pigment in chloroplasts that absorbs light energy for the process of photosynthesis

Chloroplast (1.1)   organelle containing chlorophyll; the site of photosynthesis

Chromatid (1.3)   replicated copy of a chromosome visible during cell division

Chromosome (1.3)   structure containing hereditary material; composed of DNA that codes for all the characteristics of an organism

Chromosome complement (1.3)   the characteristic number of chromosomes in a typical cell of an organism

Cilia (2.6c)   hair-like structures lining the trachea that move mucus with trapped bacteria away from the lungs (*sing.* cilium)

Community (3.1)   all the organisms living in a habitat

Competition (3.2)   interaction between organisms seeking the same limited resources

Complementary (1.4)   fitting together like a hand in a glove; applied to DNA base pairing

Concentration gradient (1.2)   difference in concentration between two solutions, cells or solutions and cells

Consumer (3.2)   animal which eats ready-made food

Coronary (2.6b)   referring to the heart and the blood vessels that serve the heart tissues

Cytoplasm (1.1)   jelly-like liquid containing cell organelles and the site of many chemical reactions

Decomposers (3.2)   organisms such as bacteria and fungi responsible for the breakdown of dead organic material

Denaturation (1.5)   change in the shape of molecules of protein such as enzymes, resulting in them becoming non-functional

Denitrifying bacteria (3.2)   convert nitrates in the soil into nitrogen gas, which is released into the atmosphere

Diffusion (1.2)   passive movement of molecules from an area of high concentration to an area of lower concentration

Digestion (2.6c)   breakdown of large, insoluble food molecules into smaller, soluble ones

Diploid (1.3)   describes a cell containing two sets of chromosomes

Discontinuous (2.5)   alternative term for discrete variation, which is variation that is clear-cut and observable as categories

Discrete (2.5)   variation that is clear-cut and observable as categories

DNA (1.1)   deoxyribonucleic acid; substance in chromosomes that carries the genetic code of an organism

Dominant (2.5)   form of a gene that is expressed in the phenotype, whether homozygous or heterozygous

Donor (1.6)   organism from which the genetic material is obtained for transfer to another species

Double-stranded helix (1.4)   describes the spiral ladder shape of DNA molecules

Ecosystem (3.1)   natural biological unit composed of habitats, populations and communities

Endocrine gland (2.3b)   gland that produces and releases a hormone directly into the blood

Enzyme (1.5)   protein produced by living cells that acts as a biological catalyst

Equator (1.3)   middle position in a cell where chromosomes attach to the spindle during mitosis

Ethanol (1.8)   alcohol produced as a result of fermentation of sugars by yeast

Family tree (2.5)   diagram that shows the inheritance of a genetic condition in a family

Fauna (3.1)   the animals of a particular region

Fermentation (1.8)   respiration without oxygen

Fertilisation (2.4)   the fusion of gametes

Fertiliser (3.5)   chemical added to the soil to improve plant growth or crop yield

Flora (3.1)   the plants of a particular region

Fungal cell (1.1)   individual cell of a fungus

Gamete (2.4)   sex cell containing the haploid chromosome number

Gene (1.4)   small section of DNA that codes for the production of a specific protein

Genetic code (1.4)   code formed by the sequence of the bases in DNA that determines an organism's characteristics

Genetic counselling (2.5)   medical procedure in which individuals can receive advice and information about an inherited condition

Genetic engineering (1.6)   the artificial transfer of genetic information from one donor cell or organism to another

Genetically modified (GM) (3.5)   term given to a cell or organism that has had its genetic code altered, usually by adding a gene from another organism

Genotype (2.5)   the alleles that an organism has for a particular characteristic, usually written as symbols

Glucagon (2.3b)   hormone produced by the pancreas, responsible for triggering the conversion of glycogen into glucose in the liver

Glucose (1.8)   simple sugar used as a respiratory substrate for the production of ATP

Glycogen (2.3b)   animal storage carbohydrate located in the liver and muscle tissues

Grazing (3.1)   method of feeding on plants by herbivores

Guard cells (2.6a)   found on either side of a stoma; they control gas exchange in leaves by controlling opening and closing of the stoma

Habitat (3.1)   the place where an organism lives

Habitat destruction (3.1)   human destruction of natural habitat by activities such as deforestation and over-grazing livestock on natural grassland

Haemoglobin (2.6b)   pigment in red blood cells that transports oxygen as oxyhaemoglobin

Heart (2.6b)   muscular organ that pumps blood around the body

Herbivore (3.2)   consumer which eats plants

Heterozygous (2.5)   describes a genotype in which the two alleles for the characteristic are different

Homozygous (2.5)   describes a genotype in which the two alleles for the characteristic are the same

Hormone (1.5)   protein released by an endocrine gland into the blood to act as a chemical messenger

Indicator species (3.5)   organisms that by their presence, abundance or absence give information such as level of pollution in the environment

Insulin (2.3b)   hormone produced by the pancreas that triggers the conversion of glucose into glycogen in the liver

Interspecific competition (3.2)   competition between organisms of two different species for a common resource

Intraspecific competition (3.2)   competition between organisms within the same species

Iodine solution (1.7)   brown-coloured solution that turns blue-black with starch

Lacteal (2.6c)   central vessel in the villi responsible for the absorption of fats

Lactic acid (1.8)   substance produced during fermentation in animals and responsible for muscle fatigue

Lifestyle choice (2.7)   decisions on lifestyle that impact on an individual's health

Light-dependent stage (1.7)   first stage in photosynthesis producing hydrogen and ATP required in the carbon fixation stage

Lignin (2.6a)   carbohydrate material lining the xylem vessels and providing strength and support

Limiting factor (1.7)   a variable that, when in short supply, can limit the rate of a chemical reaction such as photosynthesis

Lipid (1.2)   fat or oil with molecules composed of fatty acids and glycerol

Liver (2.3b)   large organ, beside the stomach, with many important functions including a role in blood glucose control

Lungs (2.6c)   organs responsible for gas exchange in mammals, birds, reptiles and amphibians

Lymph (2.6c)   liquid that circulates within a mammal's body, transporting the products of fat digestion from the lacteals

Medium (1.3)   solid or liquid nutrient agar or broth used to culture microorganisms

Medulla (2.3a)   part of the brain controlling breathing, heart rate and peristalsis

Meristem (2.2)   localised region of actively dividing cells in plants

Messenger RNA (mRNA) (1.4)   substance that carries a complementary copy of the genetic code from DNA to the ribosomes

Minerals (2.6a)   nutrient ions essential for healthy growth

Mitochondrion (1.1)   organelle that is the site of aerobic respiration and ATP production in cells (*pl.* mitochondria)

Mitosis (1.3)   division of the nucleus of a cell that leads to the production of two genetically identical diploid daughter cells

Motile (2.4)   able to move under its own power

Motor neuron (2.3a)   nerve cell that carries electrical impulses from the CNS to effectors such as muscles or glands

Mucus (2.6c)   sticky substance lining the trachea and bronchi, trapping dust and bacteria

Multicellular (1.1)   having many cells

Mutation (3.4)   a random and spontaneous change in the structure of a gene, chromosome or number of chromosomes; only source of new alleles

Nerves (2.3a)   specialised tissues that connect receptors to the CNS and the CNS to the effectors

Neuron (2.3a)   nerve cell that is specialised to transmit electrical impulses

Niche (3.1)   the role an organism has within its community in an ecosystem

Nitrifying bacteria (3.2)   produce nitrate, which is released into soil

Nitrogen cycle (3.2)   sequence of events or processes involved in the recycling of nitrogen

Nitrogen-fixing bacteria (3.2)   bacteria found free living in the soil or in the root nodules of some plants that convert nitrogen gas into nitrate

Nucleus (1.1)   organelle that is the control centre of a cell containing the genetic information of the organism (*pl.* nuclei)

Omnivore (3.2)   consumer which eats a mixture of plants and animals

Optimum (1.5)   conditions such as temperature and pH at which an enzyme works best

Organ (2.1)   a group of different tissues that work together to carry out a particular function, e.g. heart and lungs

Organelle (1.1)   membrane-bound compartment with a specific function in animal, plant and fungal cells

Osmosis (1.2)   movement of water molecules from an area of high to an area of lower water concentration through a selectively permeable membrane

Ova (2.4)   female gametes produced by ovaries in animals (*sing.* ovum)

Ovaries (2.4)   female sex organs (*sing.* ovary)

Over-exploitation (3.1)   human activities, such as over-fishing, over-hunting and over-grazing, that cause extinctions and destroy the food web balance

Ovule (2.4)   structure containing a female gamete, produced by ovaries in plants

Pancreas (2.3b)   organ responsible for the production of digestive enzymes and the hormones insulin and glucagon

Passive transport (1.2)   movement of molecules without the need for additional energy, e.g. diffusion and osmosis

Peristalsis (2.6c)   waves of muscular contraction responsible for the movement of food through the intestines

Pesticides (3.5)   general name for chemicals used to kill organisms that damage or feed on crop plants

Phenotype (2.5)   the visible characteristics of an organism that occur as a result of its genes

Phloem (2.6a)   vessels in plants that transport sugars

Photosynthesis (1.1)   process carried out by green plants to make their own food using light energy

Pitfall trap (3.3)   sampling technique used to trap animals living on the soil surface or in leaf litter

Plasmid (1.1)   circular genetic material present in bacterial cells and used in genetic engineering or modification

Plasmolysed (1.2)   description of a plant cell in which the vacuole has shrunk and the membrane has pulled away from the wall due to water loss

Poles (1.3)   opposite ends of a cell to which chromatids migrate during mitosis

Pollen grain (2.4)   structure produced in the anthers of a flower that contains the male gamete

Pollination (2.4)   transfer of a pollen grain from anther to stigma, usually by wind or an animal pollinator

Pollution (3.1)   environmental damage caused by humans usually by release of substances to the environment

Polygenic (2.5)   inheritance determined by the interaction of several genes acting together

Precipitation (3.1)   water such as rain, snow, sleet, hail, dew

Predation (3.1)   obtaining food by hunting and killing prey organisms

Producer (3.2)   organism that synthesises its own food

Product (1.5)   substance made by an enzyme-catalysed reaction

Protein (1.1)   substance composed of chains of amino acids and containing the elements carbon, hydrogen, oxygen and nitrogen

Pulmonary artery (2.6b)   artery carrying deoxygenated blood from the heart to the lungs

Pulmonary vein (2.6b)   vein carrying oxygenated blood to the heart from the lungs

Pyramid of biomass (3.2)   diagram that shows the relative total masses of the organisms at each level in a food chain

Pyramid of energy (3.2)   diagram that shows the relative quantities of energy at each level in a food chain

Pyramid of numbers (3.2)   diagram that shows the relative numbers of organisms at each level in a food chain

Pyruvate (1.8)   substance produced by the breakdown of glucose in the cytoplasm in fermentation or during the first stage of aerobic respiration

Quadrat (3.3)   square frame of known area used for sampling the abundance and distribution of slow or non-moving organisms

Qualitative (3.3)   able to be expressed as presence or absence; referring to results from sampling

Quantitative (3.3)   able to be expressed using numerical values; referring to results from sampling

Radiation (3.4)   energy in wave form such as light, sound, heat, X-rays, gamma rays

Receptor cell (2.3a)   cell that can detect stimuli inside or outside the body

Receptor protein (1.5)   cell surface protein which allows a cell to recognise specific substances

Recessive (2.5)   allele of a gene that only shows in the phenotype if the genotype is homozygous for that allele

Recipient (1.3)   a cell or organism that receives genetic material from a donor cell or organism

Red blood cell (2.6b)   blood cell containing the pigment haemoglobin responsible for the transport of oxygen

Reflex arc (2.3a)   pathway of information from a sensory neuron through a relay neuron directly to a motor neuron

Relay neuron (2.3a)   nerve cell that transmits electrical impulses from sensory neurons to motor neurons

Replication (1.3)   copying of DNA to produce chromatids before mitosis

Respiration (1.8)   a series of enzyme-controlled reactions resulting in the production of ATP from the chemical energy in glucose

Ribosome (1.1)   site of protein synthesis

Root epidermis (2.6a)   outer layer of cells of a root

Root hair cell (2.6a)   specialised cell that increases the surface area of the root epidermis to improve the uptake of water and minerals

Root nodule (3.2)   small swelling on the roots of plants such as peas, beans and clover that contains nitrogen-fixing bacteria

Sample (3.3)   a representative part of a larger quantity

Selection pressure (3.4)   factor such as predation or disease that affects a population, resulting in the death of some individuals and survival of others

Selective advantage (3.4)   an increased chance of survival for an organism because of possession of favourable characteristics

Selectively permeable (1.2)   refers to a membrane that controls the movement of certain molecules depending on their size

Sense organs (2.3a)   organs with receptor cells adapted to detect specific stimuli

Sensory neuron (2.3a)   nerve cell that transmits electrical impulses from a sense organ to the CNS

Source of error (3.3)   the origin of a mistake in drawing conclusions from experiments

Specialised (2.1)   description of a cell that has become differentiated to carry out a particular function

Speciation (3.4)   formation of two or more species from an original ancestral species

Species (3.4)   organisms with similar characteristics and with the ability to interbreed to produce fertile offspring

Specific (1.5)   each different enzyme acts on one substrate only

Sperm cell (2.4)   gamete produced in the testes of male animals

Spinal cord (2.3a)   part of the central nervous system of a mammal that runs within its backbone

Spindle fibres (1.3)   protein threads produced during mitosis to pull chromatids apart

Spongy mesophyll (2.6a)   plant leaf tissue with loosely packed cells and air spaces between them to allow gas exchange

Starch (1.7)   storage carbohydrate in plants

Stem cell (2.2)   unspecialised cell capable of dividing into cells that can develop into different cell types

Stimuli (2.3a)   changes in the environment detected by receptor cells that trigger a response in an organism (*sing.* stimulus)

Stomata (2.6a)   tiny pores in the leaf epidermis that allow gas exchange (*sing.* stoma)

Structural (1.5)   referring to the proteins in membranes, muscle, bone, hair, nails etc.

Substrate (1.5)   the substance on which an enzyme works

Sugar (1.7)   energy-rich sub-units made by green plants in photosynthesis that can join into larger carbohydrates such as starch

Synapse (2.3a)   gap between two neurons

System (2.1)   a group of organs that work together to carry out a particular function, e.g. circulatory, respiratory and digestive

Target organ (2.3b)   organ with receptor molecules on its cell surfaces that recognise a specific hormone

Testes (2.4)   male sex organs in animals for the production of sperm

Tissue (2.1)   a group of similar cells carrying out the same function

Toxicity (3.5)   poison level

Transforming (1.6)   modification of an organism genetically by genetic engineering

Transpiration (2.6a)   evaporation of water through the stomata of leaves

Turgid (1.2)   description of a swollen plant cell with a full vacuole resulting from water intake due to osmosis

Ultrastructure (1.1)   fine structure and detail of a cell and its organelles revealed by an electron microscope

Unicellular (1.1)   single-celled

Vacuole (1.1)   membrane-bound sac containing cell sap in plant and fungal cells

Valve (2.6b)   structure in veins that prevents the backflow of blood

Variation (2.5)   differences in characteristics that can be seen between individual members of a species

Vascular tissue (2.6a)   plant tissue consisting of phloem and xylem that transports material in a plant

Vector (1.6)   method of transferring genetic material from a donor to a recipient, e.g. viruses, bacterial cells or plasmids

Vein (2.6b)   general name for a blood vessel with valves that transports blood to the heart

Vena cava (2.6b)   vein carrying deoxygenated blood to the heart from the body systems

Ventricles (2.6b)   lower chambers of the heart that receive blood from the atria and pump it into arteries

Villi (2.6c)   finger-like projections of the small intestine lining providing a large surface area for absorption of food (*sing.* villus)

Virus (1.6)   microorganism that can be used in the transfer of genetic information

Xylem vessels (2.6a)   narrow, dead tubes with lignin in their walls for the transport of water and minerals in plants

Yeast (1.8)   unicellular fungus used commercially in the brewing and baking industries

Zygote (2.4)   fertilised egg cell